Automotive Engineering Plastics

Automotive Engineering Plastics

Richard Wood

PENTECH PRESS
London

First published 1991
by Pentech Press Limited
Graham Lodge, Graham Road
London NW4 3DG

APR 21 '00

© Richard Wood, 1991

British Library Cataloguing in Publication Data
Wood, Richard, *1915–*
    Automotive engineering plastics
    1. Cars. Plastics. Components. Production
    I. Title
    629.234

    ISBN 0-7273-0115-2

Printed in Great Britain

Preface

The development and application of plastics materials with specific properties is now wider and more sophisticated in the passenger car industry than in any other area of engineering. The technology associated with the development of polymers and polymer composites as replacements for metals aimed at effecting weight reduction and facilitating assembly in production has been the responsibility of both material producers and automobile engineers alike.

The application of plastics to all areas of modern automotive engineering is now extensive and embraces in addition to bodywork, chassis and engine bay components, electrics, control and transmission systems while the earliest applications of plastics as replacements for leather and cloth has extended to all aspects of interior trim to include coverings for safety fascias, seats, door and roof linings.

Since the introduction of reinforcement in the early 1950s combinations of polyester and to a lesser extent epoxide resins and glass fibre have been used in vehicle bodywork. While these materials offer the constructor advantages of lightness, corrosion resistance and a marked reduction in tooling costs, their use for complete bodywork has largely been confined to specialised and comparatively small output producers due to the length of the operation and curing cycles involved. In highly specialised applications such as racing car chassis and body construction the development of high cost, extremely high strength carbon fibre as a reinforcement for epoxide and other resins has revolutionised weight savings and has vastly increased impact resistance and thus driver safety in monocoque constructions. In more recent years, however, developments in the properties of reinforced thermoset composites such as sheet moulding compound (SMC) has brought these materials into greater prominence. Similarly, advances in the properties and production methods as applied to reinforced thermoplastics which can be injection moulded in conventional cycle times has permitted their use in large scale bodywork production.

Currently, considerable information exists in company literature regarding the use of polymers and polymer combinations in vehicle construction. This information is, however, somewhat fragmented taking the form of catalogue material and technical papers dealing with highly specialised applications. I have, therefore, attempted to bring together in one volume much of this diverse information and to review the wide range of materials available and their application in the modern motor car.

Topics dealt with include the equipment and moulding processes used to produce various types of components in thermoset, thermoplastic, foamed and composite materials and the application of these materials in the engine bay, powertrain, chassis bodywork and electrical and control systems. Early work in the field, the application of plastics materials in experimental vehicles designed specifically to evaluate weight savings, minimise fuel consumption and to promote passenger safety is discussed, also the development of reinforcing materials and the problems, technology and advances in recycling of automotive materials. Lastly, trade names, manufacturers, and abbreviations of the more commonly used polymers and polymer composites are given together with an index and bibliography to facilitate further reading on the subject.

Richard Wood

Contents

1. **INTRODUCTION**   1
   1.1 Recycling   2
   1.2 Engineering polymers   3
   1.3 'Just in time' production systems   4

2. **PRODUCTION METHODS**   5
   2.1 Injection methods   5
   2.2 Injection moulding thermosets   7
   2.3 Injection moulding structural foam   8
   2.4 Multiple material injection moulding   10
   2.5 Gas-melt injection system   13
   2.6 Injection moulding multi-coloured components   14
   2.7 Reinforced polyester injection moulding
        (ZMC process)   16
   2.8 Composite injection moulding   17
   2.9 Insert injection moulding   17
   2.10 Fusible-core injection moulding   18
   2.11 Extrusion of tube, pipe, profile and sheet   18
   2.12 Blow moulding   19
   2.13 Vacuum and pressure forming   21
   2.14 Rotational moulding   21
   2.15 Welding   22
   2.16 Fibre-reinforced resin moulding: open and closed
        mould process   22
   2.17 Plating on plastics   24
   2.18 Moulding with a fabric finish   25

3. **POWERTRAIN**   27
   3.1 Vehicle electrics   27
   3.2 Engines, camshaft covers, oil sumps and gaskets   31
   3.3 Composite engines   33
   3.4 Fuel systems, manifolds and tanks   35
   3.5 Cooling systems   39
   3.6 Transmissions   43

4. **CHASSIS**   47
   4.1 Suspensions   47
   4.2 Steering: flexible couplings and composite steering
        wheels   50
   4.3 Braking systems   50
   4.4 Road wheels: weight saving and composites   51

	4.5	Road wheel trim	52
	4.6	Bumpers: design, weight saving, special models	54
5.	**BODYWORK**		**62**
	5.1	Application of plastics – early work	62
	5.2	Composite construction	68
	5.3	Body components: composite assemblies, doors and tailgates	70
	5.4	External safety: active and passive safety, damage limitation	73
	5.5	'Soft ends': physical requirements, deformation and materials	75
	5.6	Fascias: mouldability requirements, weight saving and integration	77
	5.7	Windows and windscreens: sealing, temperature and corrosion resistance	80
	5.8	Lights: glass replacement and rear lights	82
	5.9	Seating: regulations, weight savings, recline mechanism, foam/fabric	86
	5.10	Carpets and headliners	90
6.	**RECYCLING**		**93**
	6.1	Car population increase: dumping, routes to material recovery and sorting	93
	6.2	Overall bumper systems	95
	6.3	Interior assemblies	96
	6.4	Recycling plastics fuel tanks	97
	6.5	Composites	98
	6.6	Thermoplastic composites	99
	6.7	Current activity	100
7.	**SPECIAL CONSTRUCTION – PROTOTYPES**		**102**
	7.1	Early projects	102
	7.2	Current projects	107
	7.3	Blow-moulded body panels	107
	7.4	Du Pont APV project	108
	7.5	Carmat 2000 project	109
	7.6	Racing car research	109
8.	**REINFORCEMENT**		**112**
	8.1	Early systems	112
	8.2	Glass fibre types: rovings, sizing, density	113
	8.3	Glass fibre mat: chopped strand, needled and veil mat	113

8.4   Sheet moulding compound (SMC)   114
8.5   Glass fibre reinforced thermoplastics   114
8.6   Bulk moulding compound (BMC)   116
8.7   Carbon fibre   117

Bibliography   129

Appendix: Trade names and supplier/manufacturer   131

Index   135

1

Introduction

Plastics are now universally recognised by European and American automobile manufacturers not only as a key to achieving an improved fuel/performance ratio by replacing metal for interior body components but also as a solution to many of their manufacturing, design, styling and cost problems. The diversity of properties offered by plastics materials in general and, in particular, by the more recently developed composite materials make them attractive to the automobile engineer. The strength-to-weight ratio of reinforced materials offer the possibility of significant total weight reduction coupled with the ability of being moulded into complex shapes. Thus a single moulding can replace a costly, labour intensive, welded steel assembly such as a dashboard or console. Significantly lower tooling costs, typically one fifth, as compared with those associated with metal pressings, notably in the area of body panels, has been a further incentive to the development of materials and processing techniques. In addition to being significantly lighter, plastics body panels are considerably more durable and corrosion resistant than steel pressings. Also, the fact that their tooling is less costly permits the manufacturer and stylist more freedom to update an existing model or to replace an outdated model with a technically advanced and more visually attractive vehicle in keeping with the latest market trends.

When evaluating a changeover from traditional pressed and welded steel bodywork to plastics, either in thermoset or thermoplastic materials, the manufacturer must be assured that the new materials exhibit the required mechanical properties of stiffness and lack of creep. Additionally, for quantity production the materials must be compatable with painting in-line. These requirements must also be evaluated in relation to the capital investment involved in a changeover from and the replacement of existing tooling by a moulding process. The decisive factor will be production speed and it is this area that recent developments in equipment and techniques for the injection of reinforced thermoplastics have been of major importance.

The earlier introduction of glass fibre reinforced polyester resin

1

afforded considerably greater design freedom for the short run production of attractively styled and aerodynamically efficient bodywork such as the Corvette and the now discontinued Fiero in the United States, the Lotus range in the United Kingdom and the Matra Simca in France, among others. Later developments in moulding techniques for glass reinforced polyesters culminated in the resin injection process by Lotus which ensures consistency of part thickness, predictable glass fibre distribution and greatly improved glass/resin ratio. Disadvantages of the process as compared with the later glass reinforced polyester injection moulding process designated ZMC (Section 2.7), as developed by Billion in France, is that cycles are necessarily protracted and thus not competitive for quantity production. Components made by the injection moulding of glass-reinforced thermoplastics notably nylon and polypropylene, which offer the physical properties demanded by automotive applications, also confer the important advantage of a recycling capability.

With current environmental pressure to reduce fuel consumption and exhaust emission, and to improve aerodynamic efficiency, the plastics content of the average car will inevitably continue to increase. The emphasis will be on developing materials for use in all areas of the vehicle and in particular the bodywork. However, while the day of the 'all plastic' car in which the entire load bearing structure is of plastics materials can be anticipated, its realisation cannot be forecast.

1.1 RECYCLING

One problem which is current and can be forecast to increase is the disposal or preferably the recycling of the increasingly large plastics content of vehicles which will become redundant in future years. Where large assemblies of thermoplastics parts are concerned, such as fascias, bumpers and fuel tanks and with the anticipated increase in the use of these materials in body panelling, the problem is alleviated if the materials can be recycled and subsequently remoulded for use in a similar or less critical applications. As detailed in Chapter 6, considerable efforts are currently being made in this direction, both in Europe and the United States. In Europe, Dutch State Mines (DSM) are in collaboration with Audi Volkswagen in the reclaim, remoulding and re-use of Volkswagen modified polypropylene bumpers. Other major reclaim operations are being set-up variously by Du Pont and General Electric Plastics in Europe and Connell, among others, in the United States. The recovery of glass reinforced polypropylene is being assessed by BASF.

The reclaim of sheet moulding materials (SMC) however, poses additional problems. These materials which already form a considerable percentage of the bodywork of some models have thermosetting characteristics and thus cannot be melted and remoulded. They can, however, be granulated and used in suitable proportions as extenders or fillers with virgin thermoplastic materials for less critical applications or possibly as extenders in the core layer of sandwich mouldings. Other avenues being examined include various pyrolysis and chemical recovery techniques which are designed to reclaim the reinforcement. These techniques will no doubt receive more attention as the use of high-strength, high-cost aramid and carbon fibre reinforcement for critical applications increases.

1.2 ENGINEERING POLYMERS

An important area of advance already influencing the use of plastics in the modern car, the impact of which will increase, has been the development of the so called 'engineering polymers' having physical properties which overcome the limitations of traditional materials with regard to tensile strength, resistance to stress creep and the capability to withstand high operating temperatures. To meet the economic demands of quantity production these new materials, largely designed to replace metals in some applications, must also be capable of being moulded or formed on fast cycles and, as a finished product, to be competitive with metals. Parallel with the development of materials with the required physical properties have been advances in processing techniques which permit assemblies and output to be economic with regard to speed and labour content. Among these have been developments in equipment for moulding long glass fibre reinforced thermoplastics – a technique which is being applied to the production of exterior body panels. The process has a twofold advantage in that it can be carried out in normal cycle times and that the material can be recycled. Earlier developments in the area of large panel production have included advanced equipment for the sandwich moulding of items such as door, bonnet and tailgate panels (Section 2.4). In the injection process an inner layer, which can be of reclaimed material, affords the necessary stiffness with the minimum of ribbing. A more recent technique which is being used increasingly for smaller items consists of introducing gas, usually nitrogen or air under pressure, simultaneously with injection of the polymer into a closed mould. The resultant hollow mouldings are thus lighter and exhibit a substantially greater stiffness than a similar sized solid moulding.

1.3 'JUST IN TIME' PRODUCTION SYSTEM

For many years accepted practice in the moulding shop has been to set-up an injection machine for as long a run as possible of a given item. The reason has been that many moulds, particularly in the automotive industry, are exceedingly large and heavy and thus require considerable time and labour for transport, mounting, coupling the various services and for the setting-up and try-out of the new processing conditions. Today with storage space at a premium and labour costs high there has been a trend to produce parts as they are required on the production assembly line. This system, known as 'Just in Time' or 'JIT' production, saves parts handling and storage space and thus has resulted in increased efficiency and a reduction in costs. Introduction of the system has been made possible by a number of developments. Firstly, the modern injection machine is controlled digitally with the facility for calling-up an entire set of previously established processing parameters stored in a computer bank. Secondly, the advent of overall computer control permits moulds to be selected from storage and, in the more sophisticated systems, to be transported by robot trolley to and from the moulding machine. Thirdly, various automatic quick change systems now exist for mounting the mould automatically and connecting the heating and cooling circuits. All the operator has to do is to key in the required programme for production of the new part from the memory bank. In some systems means now exist for preheating the new mould before the changeover, thus further reducing machine downtime.

As the following chapters indicate the future for plastics in the vehicle field is extremely bright. However, cooperation between car manufacturers and materials manufacturers, already considerable, will continue to be vital to maximise the benefits the change to plastics can offer. Developments in electronics offer an increasing outlet for plastics. The proportion of the cost of a car today accounted for by electronic components and assemblies will increase from the current 15% to well over 20%, highlighting the need for continued development of suitable polymer materials.

2
Production methods

2.1 INJECTION MOULDING

The injection process in its various forms is the basic method of producing components from the wide range of thermoplastic polymers available today. It is being used increasingly by the automotive industry to produce not only medium sized components but also to mould large body parts hitherto fabricated as sheet metal assemblies. Advantages of the process stem from the capability of the automotive designer to replace complex metal assemblies with a lighter, one-piece component that can be produced repetitively in the finished state at a single machine cycle. In view of recent developments that have taken place in the application of the process in bodywork and other areas of the passenger car, a brief description of the basic process and its more important variants is given here.

In principle, the process consists of injecting a plasticised thermoplastic polymer into a closed mould under conditions of controlled time and pressure. Polymer, usually in the form of granulate, is hopper fed to the feed section of a reciprocating screw operating in a heated barrel. The screw revolves at a comparatively low speed so that the granulate is melted and homogenised as it is heated and transported forward by the screw flights. The screw retracts under the back pressure of the melt as the latter collects at the screw tip prior to the injection cycle. When a full shot of material has been transported screw rotation is stopped, a non-return valve is closed and the screw reciprocated to inject the material into the mould. At the end of a predetermined hold-on and cooling period, screw rotation is initiated and the plasticising and injection cycle repeated.

In reciprocating screw injection machines screw rotation is by electric motor drive via a speed reducing gear train, (Figure 2.1) or in some cases by hydraulic motor (Figure 2.2). Linear movement of the injection unit carriage to bring the injection nozzle into pressure contact with the sprue bush in the mould is effected by hydraulic cylinders. Forward movement of the screw during the injection

5

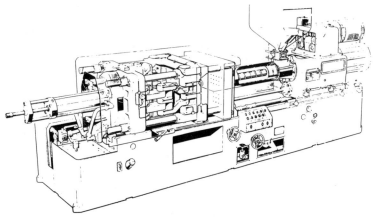

Fig. 2.1   Example of a reciprocating screw injection machine with electric motor, gear driven screw and hydraulic injection cylinder. Mould clamping is by hydraulically actuated, double shear link type toggles. (Courtesy Herbert Machinery)

cycle is under the control of a separate hydraulic system (Figure 2.2).

Because injection moulding is a mass production process considerations of long life, dimensional accuracy and reproducibility are of paramount importance and determine the design and material of which the mould is constructed. Moulds for automotive work are necessarily costly and usually made of some type of oil-hardened stainless steel. In some cases areas of polymer contact are hard chromium plated. In general mould temperature control is by means of integral water circulation passages with, depending on the design, embedded heating elements in certain areas.

Injection moulds consist of two separate units, one mounted on

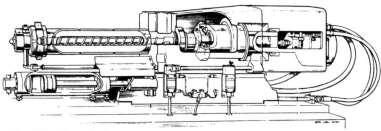

Fig. 2.2   The injection unit of a reciprocating screw injection machine with hydraulically operated screw rotation, injection and injection carriage movement. (Courtesy Machines Billion)

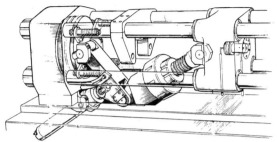

Fig. 2.3   Principle of a single hydraulically operated mould clamping unit with a pressure cushion for applying final locking pressure. (Courtesy Machines Billion)

the fixed platen and carrying the injection sprue and the other mounted on the moving platen of the machine. The latter is actuated over the opening and closing stages either by a toggle mechanism (Figures 2.1 and 2.3), or by the direct action of an hydraulic cylinder. Locking or clamping pressure to ensure that the mould remains closed against injection pressure is of the order of tons or hundreds of tons depending on the size of the machine and the projected area of the moulding. On mould opening, the moulding is ejected by various means, some mechanical which are linked to the opening mechanism, others are operated hydraulically in sequence with the opening cycle. Needless to say the majority of medium and large injection machines are now digitally controlled with regard to temperature, pressure, speed and operational sequence.

2.2   INJECTION MOULDING THERMOSETS

Briefly, the advantages of injection thermosets include the elimination of flash on the component, close dimensional tolerance and the avoidance of the need to use tabletting and preheating equipment associated with compression moulding. While the basic principle of the equipment is similar to that of thermoplastic injection machines, features include specially designed heating cylinders and screws with close control of temperature in the plasticising stage to eliminate danger of pre-curing. In most cases both die halves are held at different temperatures for optimum results.

Thermosets offer excellent electrical insulation properties and heat resistance and find application in the engine bay in ignition and associated small size equipment. Variants of the machine take the form of a horizontal injection unit and conventional clamp in-line or a horizontal injection unit used in conjunction with a vertical clamp unit.

While discussing methods of moulding thermoset materials mention should be made of compression moulding. This process, while not allied to the injection principle and because of functional limitations is only used to produce small parts, is the original method of moulding plastics. It consists basically of compressing pre-heated thermoset powder or granule in a heated mould. For quantity production the method is usually associated with multi-mould carousel type equipment.

2.3 INJECTION MOULDING STRUCTURAL FOAM

Structural foam is defined as a plastic product having integral skins, a cellular core and a sufficiently high strength-to-weight ratio to be classed as structural. The loose definition allows for many varieties of the concept in which fairly low viscosity, multi-component, reactive liquids are mixed and injected into closed moulds. It includes both thermoplastic and thermoset polymers and covers a wide range of densities.

Processes include injection moulding by low pressure, gas injection and high pressure techniques. In the low pressure process a chemical blowing agent is dry blended with the resin prior to its being charged into the hopper, (Figure 2.4). During processing the blowing agent decomposes with heat and releases gas into the melt. In the technique a metered, short shot is injected at high speed. Normally some 0.2 to 1.5% of blowing agent by weight with resin will produce parts with good foaming properties. In the gas injection process the resin melt is mixed with nitrogen which is injected direct into the barrel, (Figure 2.5). The gaseous melt is

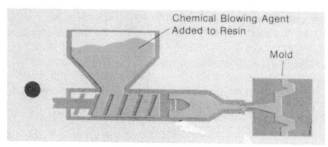

Fig. 2.4   The low pressure or chemical system of moulding foam. (Courtesy Plastics Machinery & Equipment Magazine)

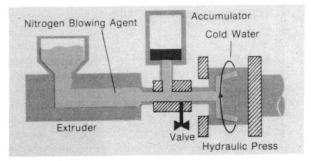

Fig. 2.5   The nitrogen system for the injection of moulded foam. (Courtesy Plastics Machinery & Equipment Magazine)

then fed into an accumulator which holds it under pressure to prevent premature expansion until a predetermined shot is built-up. When the correct shot size is attained the valve opens and the accumulator ram descends to feed the melt into the mould. At this point the mould is only partially filled. Because the mould is under low pressure, the gaseous polymer expands to completely fill the cavity.

In the high pressure injection method with expansion moulds, the mould is completely filled before the foaming action commences, (Figure 2.6). This results in a solid skin free of gas splay marks and a void-free closed-cell uniform interior. Complete mould filling prior to the onset of foaming also has the effect of closely controlling the foaming action. Foaming is carried out without any large scale material migration, thus avoiding voids and giving a closed cell structure which is impermeable and will absorb no moisture. The density of the moulded part produced by this process can be accurately and consistently controlled by establishing the ratio of starting volume to end product volume. The density range depends on the resin being processed but most unmodified resins can be moulded with a specific gravity as low as 0.25. Foaming agents may be added to the polymer in hopper-blenders. Pre-blended resins are also available while a third method is the use of foam concentrates.

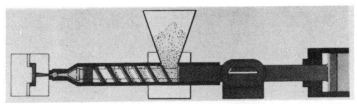

Fig. 2.6   The high presure foaming system with expansion moulds. (Courtesy Plastics Machinery & Equipment Magazine)

2.4 MULTIPLE MATERIAL INJECTION MOULDING

In this technique two resins are used to combine the advantages of a
smooth surface, achieved by conventional injection moulding, with
the advantages of a structural foam core to give rigidity in
components such as generally flat boot, bonnet and door panels.

Two resins are injected into a common sprue through a specially
designed nozzle (Figure 2.7) that connects to two conventional
reciprocating screw injection units or through a two-channel nozzle
that permits a period of simultaneous injection of both components.
Different resins can be used for skin and core, thus providing the
opportunity to reduce average material costs as reground material

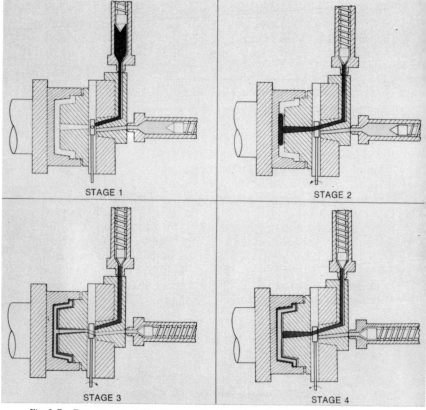

STAGE 1   STAGE 2

STAGE 3   STAGE 4

*Fig. 2.7   Four stages in filling the mould in the ICI sandwich-moulding process. First,
the skin is injected, then the core polymer. Finally, the skin polymer is injected to clear
the strue and seal the skin. (Courtesy ICI)*

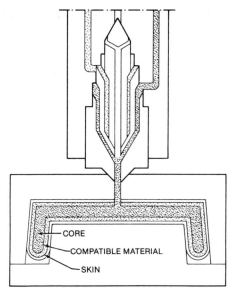

Fig. 2.8 Sliding shut-offs in the nozzle permit sequential injection in three-material mould. A small amount of the skin material will be injected in the fourth stage to seal-off the gate. (Courtesy Machines Billion)

can be used in the core. Additionally, using different resins for skin and core can enhance the mechanical and physical properties. High impact resin may be used for the skin and a high modulus resin for the core. Combinations of a relatively soft resin for the skin and a hard foamed core are also possible.

For applications in which the component is produced from two

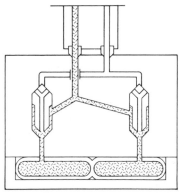

Fig. 2.9 Achieving uniform material thickness in large parts requires more than one injection point. (Courtesy Machines Billion)

incompatible polymers a three-material system overcomes the problems of poor adhesion by interposing a mutually compatible polymer layer between the inner and outer skins. The triple-material injection nozzle (Figure 2.8) has multiple feed channels and internal sliding shut-offs. It operates sequentially; first injecting the outer skin layer, then after shut-off the central channel, the interposed layer is injected. The shut-off of this channel is closed and the core material is injected into the centre of the previous material forcing it outwards to fill the mould. Moulding of large multi-material components requires several injection points to ensure regularity of skin, intermediate layer and core thickness (Figure 2.9). Polymer compatability is shown in Figure 2.10.

	ABS	ASA	CA	EVA	PA6	PA66	PC	PE-HD	PE-LD	PMMA	POM	PP	PPO-MOD	PS-GP	PS-HI	PBTP	TPU	PVC-W	SAN	TPR	PETP	PVAC	PPSU	PC-PBTP	PC-ABS
ABS	G	G	G				G	N	N	G		N	N	N	N	G	G	G	G		G		P	G	G
ASA	G	G	G	G			G	N	N	G		N	N	N	N	G	G	G	G				P	G	G
CA	G	G	G	P				N	N			N	N	N	N	G	G	G	G						
EVA		G	P	G			G	G		G		G					N								
PA6					G	G		P	P			P		N	N		G								
PA66					G	G	P	P	P			P		N	N		G								
PC	G	G				P	G	N	N			N		N	N	G	G	G	G		G		G	G	G
PE-HD	N	N	N	G	P	P	N	G	G	P	P	N		N	N	N	N	P	N					N	N
PE-LD	N	N	N	G	P	P	N	G	G	P	P	G		N	N	N	N		N					N	N
PMMA	G	G					P	P	G			P		N	N		G	G							
POM							P	P			G	P		N	N										
PP	N	N	N	G	P	P	N	N	G	P	P	G	P	N	N	N	N	P	N	G				N	N
PPO-MOD	N	N	N										P	G	G	G	N	N	N	N				N	N
PS-GP	N	N	N	G	N	N	N	N	N	N	N	N	G	G	G	N	N	P	N					N	N
PS-HI	N	N	N		N	N	N	N	N	N	N	N	G	G	G	N	N	P	N					N	N
PBTP	G	G	G				G	N	N			N	N	N	N	G	G	G	G						
TPU	G	G	G		G	G	G	N	N			N	N	N	N	G	G	G	G						
PVC-W	G	G	G	N			G	P		G		P	N	P	P	G	G	G	G						G
SAN	G	G	G				G	N	N	G		N	N	N	N	G	G	G	G		G		P	G	G
TPR																G				G					
PETP	G															G					G			G	G
PVAC	P	P																				P		G	
PPSU							G																G		
PC-PBTP	G	G					G	N	N			N	N	N	N	G				G				G	
PC-ABS	G	G					G	N	N			N	N	N	N	G	G			G					G

Fig. 2.10 Figure indicating the varying compatibility of different polymers used in multi-material injection moulding: G = Good, P = Poor, N = None. (Courtesy Battenfeld)

2.5 GAS MELT INJECTION SYSTEM

Recent extensions of the injection process include the gas melt system designed for the production of thick-walled or voluminous parts with a varied wall thickness. Essentially the process consists of injecting gas under pressure into the melt either sequentially or in

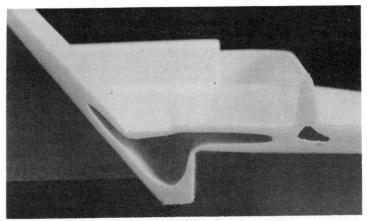

Fig. 2.11 Section through a part moulded by the 'Airmould' process. (Courtesy Battenfeld)

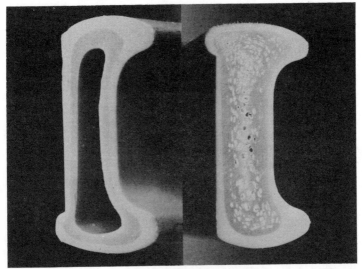

Fig. 2.12 Section through a part moulded by the 'Multifoam' process. (Courtesy Battenfeld)

parallel with injection. In the sequential variant of the technique, gas is fed into the melt already in the mould. The moment at which the gas is injected can be pre-selected as a function of time, screw stroke, melt pressure or hydraulic pressure. In a manner similar to the two-component process, gas melt technology uses the fountain flow effect and frontal flow behaviour of plastics melts so ensuring that the gas flows to the fluid centre of the moulding without mixing with the material.

Other systems developed for the production of hollow core mouldings include the *airmould* process (Figure 2.11) in which nitrogen is injected into the melt via a special designed nozzle and the *multifoam* process which produces a hollow-cored foam moulding (Figure 2.12).

2.6 INJECTION MOULDING MULTI-COLOURED COMPONENTS

This variant of the injection moulding process is used widely by the automotive industry for the production of multi-coloured lenses for front and rear light clusters. Two basic systems have been in use. One involves the moulding of separate part components that are assembled in a final mould and completely overlaid with a compatible acrylic polymer. Drawbacks inherent in this process are the difficulty of maintaining part tolerances, poor weld line quality and the possibility of component damage during handling. The second system involves the use of a rotary mould assembly to mould two- or three-colour clusters. The *'three-rhythm'* process (Figure 2.13) uses side-by-side moulds, involves rotation through 120° in each phase and produces one complete lens assembly or one complete pair of lenses (right and left) at each complete cycle. The system can be used with a variation of the overlay process in which the colours are injected sequentially onto a clear-moulded body.

The cycle of the *'two-rhythm'* process, (Figure 2.14), is similar except that rotational movement is through 180° at each phase and that two colours are injected into one mould-half during each phase. Advantages are that only two moulds are required and they can be sized to produce larger lenses.

A recent system developed by Billion and Cartier in France features single mould operation with moving cores. There is a separate mould cavity for each of the three colours within a master mould body and operating in conjunction with a separate injection unit and shut-off nozzle for each colour. The system permits flexibility of colour layout and eliminates weld lines allowing a

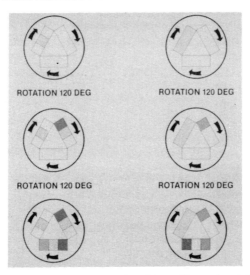

Fig. 2.13 In the 'Three-rhythm' process, the substrate of one colour is injected at one station while the other colours are injected at the other two stations. The start-up phase is shown. At left, the three-colour injection process is shown and, at right, overlay injection is depicted. (Courtesy Krauss-Maffei)

strong bond at the butt joint. Cavity movement is so rapid that no leakage from the previously injected cavity occurs. Colours are moulded in the order red/amber/clear so that dark colours do not contaminate light colours. Clamp units are vertical and injection units positioned horizontally for injection on the parting line of the mould or through a hot-runner system for inserts such as reversing light lenses.

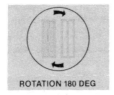 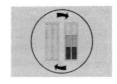

Fig. 2.14 The 'Two rhythm' process involves injection of the substrate (left) and injection of the two secondary colours at the second station (right). (Courtesy Krauss-Maffei)

2.7 REINFORCED POLYESTER INJECTION MOULDING (ZMC PROCESS)

For completeness, a catalogue of injection moulding methods should include the ZMC process developed by Billion in France for the production of large automotive parts such as boot and bonnet lids in glass reinforced polyester resin. While the process competes structurally with other body component production methods, it overcomes the many problems associated with the injection of material reinforced with glass fibres. Advantages include the facility to incorporate automatic loading of material, accurate proportioning of reinforcement without fibre breakage, rapid production and pressure programming in the mould.

The design of the injection unit permits the use of bulk moulding compound (BMC) or other prepared compounds. To avoid fibre damage the screw is stopped automatically when the feed

Fig. 2.15 An injection machine with vertical material feed for processing bulk moulding compound

mechanism from the hopper reaches its lowest limit and is ready to receive a new pre-charge. Co-ordination of the feed system with screw rotation gives an input-to-output ratio of 1:1 thus avoiding screw slip and fibre damage. Injection is effected not by screw reciprocation directly but by a combination of screw travel and the use of a sliding sleeve axial movement which is controlled by hydraulic cylinders. Unlike thermoplastics, the first thermoset material entering the mould moves to the end of the flow path. The shape and size of the injection points is of importance as fibre orientation is perpendicular to the direction of flow. Other systems for the production of smaller components include those developed in Germany by BASF and Battenfeld Berges and widely used for moulding items such as headlamp reflectors (Figure 2.15).

2.8   COMPOSITE INJECTION MOULDING

A recently developed system for the composite moulding of thermoplastics and thermosetting resins is the joint work of Nissei Plastics Industrial Co and the Three Bond Co in Japan. The system designated Hymold (Hybrid Moulding System by Double Injection) comprises an injection machine with two injection units, a liquid silicone metering device and an automatic finisher. One of the injection units supplies the thermoplastic resin, the other injects a two-component reactive hardening sealing resin. Three moulding methods can be selected. These are vertical sliding, rotating core and movable core. After primary and secondary injection, automatic removal of the part and gate cutting is carried out. The development offers the automotive industry a method of combining plastics components with a sealing material in a single operation to improve their function.

2.9   INSERT INJECTION MOULDING

This method of providing metal or pre-moulded plastics additions or attachment points such as integral threads and sockets simplifies assembly of a number of components thus reducing post moulding operations and associated labour costs. In principle the process consists of placing inserts in the specially designed mould so that the additions become an integral part of the moulding on ejection. In todays plants robots are widely used to place the inserts, the operation being sequenced with the mould-open phase.

2.10   FUSIBLE CORE INJECTION MOULDING

A fusible core system can be applied for the production of a component the configuration of which precludes the use of retractable inserts or cores. After the moulding operation, usually carried out using a reinforced, low profile bulk moulding compound or, depending on the application, an engineering polymer the low melting point alloy cores are melted out of the finished moulding. Advantages of this technique are complete design freedom irrespective of the complexity of internal passages such as, for example, an automobile induction manifold, surface smoothness of the internal ducts and the elimination of post moulding operations necessary when using conventional metal casting systems.

2.11   EXTRUSION OF TUBE, PIPE, PROFILE AND SHEET

In principle extrusion consists of plasticising a hopper fed thermoplastic polymer by means of a screw unit operating in a heated barrel and extruding the resultant melt through a die of the required configuration. Unlike the principle of the reciprocating

Fig. 2.16   Example of a pipe extrusion line. At right, the extruder, at centre, the die and at left, the downstream sizing and cooling equipment. (Courtesy Cincinnati-Milacron)

injection machine, the screw merely rotates and does not move laterally. After leaving the die, in most cases, the extrudate is passed through a vacuum sizing unit and thence through a cooling bath before being hauled-off and either coiled or, if rigid, cut automatically into predetermined lengths by a flying saw. (Figure 2.16).

Variants of the basic process include corrugation of pipe in some instances to permit flexibility, in others to increase crushing resistance. The addition of a cross-head in the die area permits the incorporation of a helical wire reinforcement in the pipe wall further to increase crushing strength. A cross-head system is also used to introduce a glass filament into the extrudate to produce an optical fibre. A recent extension of this technique is the use of two extruders operating in unison. One machine produces a light transmitting acrylic core, the second machine produces the external sheathing. In this way an optical fibre used in facia instruments can be produced in a single operation.

Developments also include the use of two extruders feeding a common die to produce a two-component profile embodying an elastomer element. The production of sheet uses the same basic extrusion equipment in conjunction with a sheet die and associated downstream wind-up machinery and, where required, embossing rolls. Extruders can be of single or twin-screw type. The latter are used widely for processing materials in powder form.

2.12 BLOW MOULDING

The basic principle of blow moulding of thermoplastics consists of heating an extruded preform to make it pliable and inflating it by means of pressurised air to conform to the internal contours of a hollow mould. For the production of large technical parts such as automobile fuel tanks, the preform, or parison is produced by extrusion with the addition of a melt accumulator to increase the shot capacity. The extrudate is passed through a die which forms it into a tube (Figure 2.17). At a predetermined length the extruder is stopped and the tube clamped between the mould halves. The mould is provided with a pinch-off at the base to close the bottom end. When fully closed a blow-pin is inserted through the top of the mould to introduce pressurised air which distends the melt to the contours of the mould. A large fuel tank blow moulding machine is shown in Figure 2.18. In cases where a single material is not able to provide the necessary gas or liquid permeation it is possible to extrude multi-layer parisons. Because a regular shaped parison is

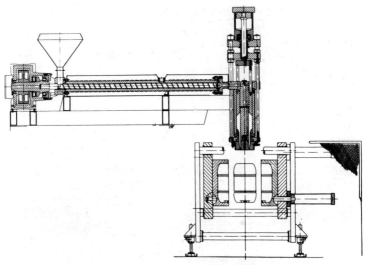

Fig. 2.17   Principle of blow moulding using an extruder and a vertical die head.
(Courtesy Hartig-Midland Ross)

stretched to fill an irregular mould there are areas where wall
thickness is reduced below that required for mechanical strength.
Modern equipment ensures that a parison is produced with varying
wall thickness to give a consistent wall thickness in the finished
moulding. Pressures involved in blow moulding are low compared
with, for example, injection moulding, thus tooling is less critical
and except for long run work, can be of cast aluminium or a suitable
alloy with intergral temperature control channels.

Blow mouldings do not necessarily have to remain hollow. The
technique can be used to produce initially a hollow part which can
be cut to produce a handed single skin part such as, for example,
two automobile door panels. The process also lends itself to inserts
and pre-moulded parts which are positioned in the mould prior to
moulding and which after the blowing operation become an integral
part of the component.

Recent developments in the area of large blow moulded
automobile fuel tanks include an off-line post moulding fluorination
process to improve the barrier properties in tanks using lead-free
petrol and the Selar process in which nylon is added at a
pre-determined concentration to the masterbatch material prior to
its being fed to the extruder. The problem of determining wall
thickness consistency in large mouldings can now be overcome by
an automatic in-mould system which alerts the operator should
thickness fall outside acceptable limits.

Fig. 2.18   A large capacity blow moulding machine for the production of automotive fuel tanks. Here the parison is extruded out to its predetermined length, stretched and sealed at the base. The mould is ready to begin its closing movement. (Courtesy Krupp-Kautex)

2.13   VACUUM AND PRESSURE FORMING

Vacuum and pressure forming of sheet thermoplastics consists basically of drawing and pressing respectively an infrared heated sheet over a male or into a shallow female mould. In the automotive industry vacuum forming processes are used to coat interior body parts with a surface skin, often using embossed sheet which can simulate a natural material finish. Formers and moulds can be of various materials and do not represent a major tooling cost.

2.14   ROTATIONAL MOULDING

Rotational moulding of hollow components such as tanks and containers consists of introducing a liquid plastics material into a heated mould which is then rotated in all directions to coat the mould interior with the melt. The process is carried out at zero pressure so tooling is comparatively inexpensive. Unlike blow moulding involving a parison, the process ensures a consistent wall thickness. No post moulding operations are required. The process is usually carried out using three-station, carousel type equipment. Rotation of the mould takes place in the first stage followed by its transfer to the cooling station and thence to the demoulding area.

2.15   WELDING

While discussing production methods mention should be made of techniques which include high frequency (HF) welding for sheet materials for applications such as interior trim and heat and friction welding. The latter processes can be used for the assembly of smaller plastics mouldings but, so far as can be ascertained, these methods do not find extensive use in the automotive industry. However, the assembly of thermoplastics components is increasingly being affected by ultrasonic welding. The cycle is fast (less than 2 seconds), the joint can be designed to be virtually flash-free, no solvents are required, labour demands are modest and the process readily adapts to automation.

An ultrasonic welder converts high frequency electrical energy to mechanical vibration and uses a probe, or horn, in contact with one of the components to be welded, transmits ultrasonic vibrations through that part to the joint surface. The other component is fixed. Friction and alternating high pressure stress-heat the touching plastics surfaces. Pressure is maintained momentarily after ultrasonic application until the joint has resolidified. The process can be applied to most thermoplastics.

2.16   FIBRE REINFORCED RESIN MOULDING:
OPEN AND CLOSED MOULD PROCESSES

The incorporation of long fibre reinforcement in liquid polyester and epoxide resins which cure by a system of molecular cross-linking in combination with a catalyst was developed largely by the aeronautical industry in the early 1950s. The process generally termed GRP in Europe and FRP in the USA, produces a combination of materials that are light, strong, weather resistant and which, by the nature of its constituents, can readily be fabricated into large and, if required, complex shapes with fibre orientation to suit the application.

The combination of these characteristics has been widely used by amateurs for automobile bodywork and currently is being used in more sophisticated forms for bodywork components and complete bodywork in limited production runs. Applications of processes that have been developed for automotive production purposes are discussed in later chapters.

As discussed in an earlier book* which dealt specifically with glass reinforced bodywork, numerous methods of moulding glass reinforced polyester and epoxide resins have been developed. They have included hand-layup, spray-layup, vacuum bag and pressure bag moulding, autoclave, cold and hot press moulding, SMC (sheet moulding compound) moulding and the resin injection – the most highly developed of the various processes currently in use by specialist manufacturers for complete bodywork production.

Hand-layup or contact moulding is the simplest method of producing resin/glass parts and lends itself particularly to short-run production of large components. A single female mould is used to give a smooth outer surface. The laminate, composed of successive layers of chopped strand glass mat is impregnated with catalysed and accelerated resin and rolled with a washer or lamb's skin roller to expel air bubbles. Curing can take place at room temperature. Spray-up is a faster method of applying fibre reinforcement and resin simultaneously to a single mould. The process is carried out with a resin spray gun in conjunction with a unit to chop reel-fed glass fibre rovings and direct the fibres into the resin stream at a predetermined rate.

Vacuum, pressure bag and autoclave methods are all extensions of the contact process and are designed to exert pressure on the laminate to improve its consolidation. Press moulding in its cold and hot forms uses preformed reinforcement and matched moulds to produce consolidation and to ensure consistency of wall thickness. Sheet moulding compound (SMC), supplied in the form of sheets of glass fibre impregnated with a catalysed polyester resin is moulded in heated, matched metal moulds on an hydraulic press. Production speeds are high with predictable glass/resin ratios.

Resin injection moulding or resin transfer moulding, of large components demands the use of a closed mould previously loaded with a predetermined quantity of reinforcement in critical areas (Figure 2.19). In some cases the injection of the catalysed and accelerated resin into the temperature controlled mould is assisted by gravity feed. In this way injection into the lightly evacuated mould relies on a combination of gravity and atmospheric pressure.

* Car Bodywork in Glass Reinforced Plastics.

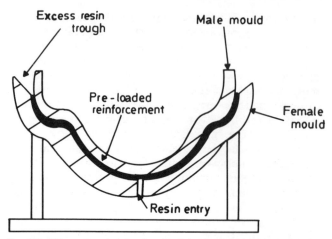

Fig. 2.19   Simplified illustration showing the principle of resin injection. Injection of the resin can be assisted by gravity or introduced more effectively by a pressure feed. Mould halves are clamped together to maintain component wall thickness during injection

Air is expelled as the mould fills. The second, or pressure process, is a faster method of injecting and completely impregnating the previously loaded reinforcement. To the specialist automobile body manufacturer, the injection technique offers deep draw facilities, the capability of using heavily filled, fire retardant resins combined with close dimensional control and automatic resin handling.

Moulds are basically similar in principle to those used in the low pressure system but are of heavier construction due to the pressures involved, which can range from 5 to 15kgf/cm². Glass reinforced polyester or glass/epoxide moulds reportedly have an average production life of 2000 and 4000 cycles, respectively. For longer runs, alloy faced moulds backed-up with reinforced epoxide resin are suitable, while for extended runs it is economic to use electroformed nickel/copper moulds suitably backed. As in all moulding operations discussed, moulds are prepared with a parting agent prior to layup. In critical cases the resin injection process can involve the use of high strength carbon fibre reinforcement and/or the inclusion of a lightweight core layer to give greater rigidity to the component without incurring a weight penalty.

2.17   PLATING ON PLASTICS

The electroplating of alloys, usually zinc based, has been in use for many years and in the automotive area has been applied largely for items such as door handles and interior furnishing details. With the more widespread use of plastics mouldings for these items considerable development has been undertaken to ensure good adhesion on various polymers. However, while the technique is still used in some applications, the trend in the modern car is to reduce the use of metallic surfaces and to introduce colour-coded styling for both interior and exterior parts. Where electronic shielding is required (Chapter 3.1), Bayer has recently introduced a range of chemicals which permit plating on difficult materials such as polyamides. The layers, usually copper and/or nickel show good adhesion and pass climatic and alternating temperature tests. An electroless system of plating on plastics is the Enshield process developed in the US by Enthone for applying a multi-layer coating of copper and nickel. The process is said to be suitable for deposition on polycarbonate and modified PPO.

2.18 MOULDING WITH A FABRIC FINISH

The combination of a rigid plastics material with a foam or fabric has been achieved notably by Hettinga in the US and has been used for interior trim. Recently developments have been introduced in Japan by the Shimizu Industry Company in conjunction with Nippondenso for the moulding of a thermoplastic component with an envelope of polyurethane foam. In Austria, Engel have developed a system for injecting a moulded plastic on to a textile with a foam backing. In the Shimizu system, two layers of foam are introduced into the mould and a plastics melt injected through one layer so that it fills the mould from between the two layers. No adhesive is required and it is claimed that the surface is free from sink marks and that finished edges are achieved. The Engel technique, designated 'Textilmelt', is said to rely on a combination of tooling 'know-how' and injection machine control and is claimed to permit the combination of a substrate and a special velvet type fabric with a soft foam backing.

Foam-in-cover seating by BASF Elastogran (Section 5.9), is produced via dual purpose equipment. Firstly, the fabric is thermoformed to shape and then backfoamed in the same mould using a RIM dispensing machine to produce a completely upholstered seat from one automatic process. The process is performed in both single-station and fourteen-station rotary machines with either dual cavity moulds or a single cavity for bench type seats. The moulding station consists of a female mould with a frame to hold the fabric, a plug assist and a male mould for foaming. The fabric which is backed by a thin layer of foam and a thermoplastic coating, is placed over the female mould and any inserts such as a wire attachment frame or polypropylene anti-squeak fabric is located in the male mould. The fabric is vacuum formed with plug assist. The frame is oscillated to eliminate any tension in the fabric. Polyurethane foam is then open poured with a robotic mix head. Dual density seating can also be poured and the mould closed for cold curing.

3

Powertrain

The use of plastics in the powertrain, ie. in the engine, engine bay, transmission, drive-line and a variety of under-bonnet auxiliaries, which include vehicle electrics and instrumentation, is discussed (Figure 3.1). As in other applications weight saving is a consideration but of greater importance in these areas are temperature resistance, good dielectric properties coupled with an ability to withstand an aggressive environment.

3.1   VEHICLE ELECTRICS

The earliest uses of plastics in the engine compartment environment were largely limited to ignition applications, such as magneto and coil distributors compression moulded in a phenolic thermoset material. Conventionally plug leads were of multi-strand copper, rubber sheathed and terminating in a simple, flattened brass fitting for connection to the plugs with a spring wire clip. Due to the heat from the engine the rubber insulation was prone to cracking with consequent electrical loss in damp weather. With the advent of heat resistant thermoplastics, distributor caps and rotors are injection moulded in a variety of mineral filled materials which offer not only excellent dielectric and heat resistant properties but also reduce 'tracking' to a minimum. Plug leads with a conductor of carbon can be crosshead extruded with a sheathing of PVC and in the majority of cases terminate in an injection moulded push-on connector or 'plug boot' which serves to shield the ceramic insulator of the plug from dust and oil and can also embody a suppressor to eliminate interference with the in-car radio. In this context, a recent development is a metallised glass-filled polyamide which can shield a variety of electronic equipment from electrical interference (Figure 3.2). Other applications of advanced polymer and polymer composites include cable insulation of temperature resistant elastomer, heat shields of fluoropolymer and baffles and covers of nylon and thermoplastic polyester.
  A current example of ignition cable development is provided by

28

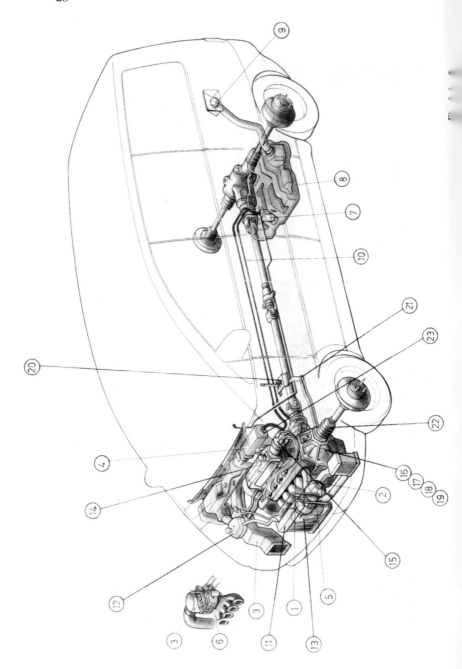

Fig. 3.1   The application of plastics and plastics composites in the powertrain of the modern automobile. (Courtesy Du Pont)

1. *Camshaft cover, cylinder head gasket reinforcement, timing belt, oil sump, oil cooler hose, oil filter housing and pick-up, throttle controls, crankcase vent hose, valve stem seals, engine mounts*
2. *Turbocharger hose*
3. *Air filter housing, air intake duct, turbo intake*
4. *Fuel filter housing, fuel injection micro circuits, fuel injector deals*
5. *Emission cannister, vacuum tubing*
6. *Carburettor body and throttle cam*
7. *Fuel pump housing*
8. *Fuel tank, diesel fuel pre-heater*
9. *Fuel filler neck and cap*
10. *Fuel hose and metal fuel line protection*
11. *Radiator end tank, water pump housing and impeller*
12. *Expansion tank*
13. *Fan, shroud and fan belt*
14. *Printed circuit boards, planar filter connectors*
15. *Coil housing, alternator cap, spark plug 'boots', bushings and seals*
16. *Clutch facing reinforcement, automatic clutch belt reinforcing*
17. *Transmission cover, gearchange linkage connectors*
18. *Transmission oil cooler hose*
19. *Automatic transmission control unit printed circuit boards*
20. *Gear lever housing and selector box*
21. *Gear change rod seals. Control cable shield*
22. *Drive shaft coupling. CVJ 'boots'. Propeller shaft composites*
23. *Electronic management interconnection assemblies*

Fig. 3.2   A metallised housing moulded in Bayer's Durethan BKV 130, glass-filled polyamide developed to shield electronic equipment in cars. (Courtesy Bayer)

Fig. 3.3   Ignition cables with a core 'Kevlar' para-aramid fibre, primary insulation of Nordel hydrocarbon rubber and a jacket of 'Hypalon' synthetic rubber are now standard on all Fiat petrol engined cars. (Courtesy Du Pont)

the high temperature resistant cable now standard on all petrol engined Fiat vehicles (Figure 3.3). The cable core is of 'Kevlar' para-aramid fibre on to which the conductive element is extruded. A primary insulation of 'Nordel' hydrocarbon rubber and a jacket of 'Hypalon' synthetic rubber are coextruded on the outside. These and other developments in the area of cable technology (such as Bayer's self-lubricating silicone rubber 'Selopren' 3285 cable insulation which facilitates installation and protects cables from damage) are due in a large part to close cooperation between the West German majors which include VW/Audi, BMW and Mercedes-Benz with leading electrical/electronic groups such as Siemans and European plastics groups including Hoechst, Bayer BASF, Rhone-Poulenc and ICI.

The electrical resistance of PVC such as Hostalit is of value in applications such as battery separators which conventionally have been produced using sintering techniques while battery cases in many instances are moulded in some form of unreinforced polypropylene such as 'Hostalen'. In the engine management system printed circuit boards are produced using dry film photoresist and solder masks. RFI/EMI protection is given by planar connectors with many flexible circuits based on various types of composites. Mass airflow sensor housings are moulded from thermoplastic polyesters.

3.2   ENGINES: CAMSHAFT COVERS, OIL SUMPS AND GASKETS

Some of the most notable examples of replacement of metals by plastics have been in the power unit itself. As in other areas reasons for the changes have been a combination of weight saving and, more importantly from the manufacturer's point of view, a combination of cost and production time. Classic examples include camshaft, timing belt and rocker box covers which for many years have consisted of sheet metal pressings or, on quality cars, of polished aluminium castings. These parts are now moulded in one of the thermoplastic polyesters with gaskets, not of conventional fabric-reinforced cork, but with one of the ethylene acrylic rubbers.

As mentioned in Section 2.8, a recently developed system permits the combination of a rigid injection moulding with an integral, semi-flexible cover-to-cylinder head sealing ring. Cam cover gaskets of ethylene-acrylic elastomer, now fitted on Daimler-Benz diesel engines, are designed to last the lifetime of the engine (Figure 3.4). These new engines have hydraulic valve tappets which never need adjustment thus permitting the use of a permanent gasket. Another example of the use of mouldings in the area is the rocker box cover on the Citroen AX which is produced in heat resistant semi-aromatic polyamide. Cylinder gaskets can be reinforced with 'Kevlar' high strength, para-amide fibre with a coating of non-stick fluorocarbon resin. The non-stick properties of these resins are also used to coat piston rings to reduce friction.

In many instances, nylon mouldings have also replaced sheet metal pressings and aluminium castings for oil sumps, oil pick-up and filter housings which in a similar manner to camshaft covers can be produced with an integral semi-flexible sump-to-cylinder block sealing gasket. A current example of weight saving is illustrated by the composite oil sump of Derakane vinyl ester resin reinforced with glass fibre. This component, produced in Dow material, is fitted to the Porsche 944 in place of an aluminium die casting. The unit is said to be 30% lighter than the aluminium casting and to cost less to produce. Studies by Porsche have shown that engine oil and cooling water temperatures increase faster with the composite sump

Fig. 3.4 Cam cover gaskets of Vamac ethylene-acrylic elastomer fitted to Daimler-Benz diesel engines using hydraulic tappets are designed to last the lifetime of the engine. (Courtesy Du Pont)

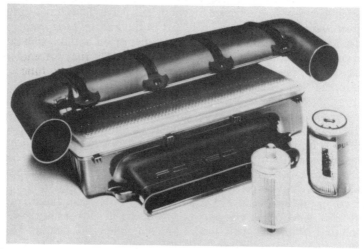

Fig. 3.5 Zytel glass-reinforced nylon air filter on the Porsche 959 turbocharged model withstands high temperatures, petrol vapour, oil and is said to eliminate sealing problems. (Courtesy Du Pont)

and so allow the engine to attain its optimum operating temperature sooner. Oil cooler hoses and crankcase hoses are often of heat, oil and ozone resistant fluorocarbon resin or synthetic rubber as are turbo charger hoses which are also required to be resistant to considerable pressure. These items are now often of ethylene-acrylic rubber reinforced with aramid fibre. Air filter housings and intake manifolds are of thermoplastic elastomer materials with turbo intake manifolds of ethylene-acrylic elastomer. An example of glass-reinforced nylon is in the air filter housing of the new four-wheel drive Porsche 959 model. The filter is located in an arduous environment because of its proximity to the 450 horsepower turbocharged 2.85 litre engine and its position under the low-level bonnet where petrol vapour and oil are present (Figure 3.5).

Another important development is engine technology is a computerised management system introduced by Brampton Renold of Calais, France which enables the camshaft advance/retard position to be monitored continuously to optimise valve timing. Designated 'Camphase', the system is intended primarily for use on engines having twin camshafts per cylinder head. It uses an ICI 'Victrex' PES polyethersulphone moulding for the linear-to-rotary piston – a key component in the system.

3.3 COMPOSITE ENGINES

While discussing applications of plastics and plastics composites in under-bonnet locations, mention should be made of developments in composite engines themselves. Since 1985 the automotive industry has known that a composite plastics engine can function successfully under adverse conditions. As stated by Owens Corning Fiberglass, endurance racing cars with 16 valve engines of glass reinforced composites have run and finished in 500km races in the USA. Components of these engines were made expensively of glass fibre reinforced epoxide pre-preg laminates and were manufactured using autoclave methods normally reserved for sophisticated aerospace applications.

Currently a reinforced plastics engine for use in standard road cars is in production in a new purpose-built plant in New Jersey, USA. It is said that the new engine (Figure 3.6) is not only economical to produce but is expected to prove cheaper than conventional metal engines as production runs rise. The plant is expected to produce 5000 engines for industrial and marine use in 1990, rising to 50,000 by 1993. To be known as the 'Polimotor' 234,

Fig. 3.6 Composite engine developed by Polimotor Research and Rogers Corporation in the USA incorporates cylinder block, cylinder head, cam cover moulded in glass reinforced thermoset resins. (Courtesy Owens Corning Fibreglass GB Ltd)

the engine is being built in a joint venture by Polimotor Research of Franklin Lakes N.J. and Rogers Corporation of Connecticut. The engine is a 2.3 litre, twin cam unit with a glass fibre reinforced cylinder block, cylinder head, oil sump and cam cover as well as several other glass reinforced components. The unit delivers 175 horsepower at 5,800 revs/min and weighs only 79kg as compared with a cast iron equivalent which weighs about double and develops 105 horsepower.

In Europe the Ford Motor Company have designed and developed a largely polymeric engine which is also lighter and said to be about a third quieter than its all-metal counterpart. The 1 litre engine which reportedly is to be installed in a Fiesta, uses metal only for the moving parts, combustion chambers and cylinders. The engine block is housed in a load-bearing assembly of 'E' glass reinforced epoxide composite mouldings bonded to the block. The assembly is supported at the rear transmission flange and front chain case. In the UK, the National Engineering Laboratory and GKN provided technical input for the project which was organised with the cooperation of the European Community programme for Basic Research in Industrial Technology. In Europe DSM Resins and DSM Research of the Netherlands, Vetrotex St Gobain of France and Galvanoform of W. Germany have all contributed to the project.

3.4   FUEL SYSTEMS, MANIFOLDS AND TANKS

Mouldings of nylon, acetal and seals of fluor-elastomer find increasing application in filter housings with extrusions of nylon in the form of tubing. Thermoplastic resins are now widely used for injection moulding carburettor bodies while variants of the fusible core technique discussed in Section 2.10 are being used more widely for the injection moulding of induction manifolds which hitherto have been produced as conventional sand castings. A recent example of the trend is the use of a bulk moulding compound in unsaturated polyester from BASF, applied by Ford in the inlet manifold of the new diesel variant of the Fiesta. A weight saving of 40% is claimed together with a temperature resistance on a continuous basis of 160°C.

The technique of fusible core moulding (Section 2.10) is also used by Ford for the intake manifold of its 1.8 litre diesel engine and by Porsche. The Ford one-piece, four cylinder manifold produced from bulk moulding compound (BMC) is approximately 40% lighter than its metal counterpart and is said to make a considerable contribution to engine performance due to its smooth inner surface and its low heat conductivity. The Porsche manifold is produced in a specially formulated 33% glass reinforced grade of ICI Maranyl nylon 66, designated 'Maranyl' A391, developed for the injection moulding of inlet manifolds. Polyacetals such as Hoechst's 'Hostaform' show to advantage for fuel accumulators such as used in the VW Golf.

Fuel tanks

The earliest experience with plastics fuel tanks dates back to the early 1950s, at a time when the first plastics brake fluid containers and fuel cans were being developed. Later Porsche 911 sports cars were equipped with 26 gallon plastics fuel tanks and Volkswagen experimented with plastics tanks in the 1973 Beetle model. In 1973

Volkswagen equipped the Passat Variant series with a 15 gallon tank in high molecular weight polyethylene. The success of these developments has led to a considerable increase in the use of blow moulded tanks with the result that sales of high density polyethylene (HDPE) fuel tanks are one of the fastest growth areas of today's automotive plastics markets. Reportedly, in North America one million tanks weighing some 7kg each were moulded in 1988. Projections double this figure for 1991 and again double the figure for the mid 1990s. Models said to have switched from steel to plastics tanks include General Motors Corsica and Ford's Thunderbird, Cougar and Escort models.

Advantages of the plastics tank as compared with the steel equivalent include increased freedom in design permitting the contours of the tank to be freely adapted to the confines of its location, the ability to hold a larger volume of fuel and, size-for-size, to be lighter. Corrosion is non-existent in a plastics tank and their performance in safety tests has been proven to be superior. These factors coupled with problem-free production methods has encouraged all leading automobile manufacturers in Europe to consider the development and use of blow moulded tanks. Without exception, tanks on European models which now include Alfa-Romeo (Italy), Citroen 2CV, Talbot, Matra Bagheera and Matra Murena, Renault 5 Turbo and Alpine (France), Saab (Sweden), Daimler-Benz 240 Diesel, Volkswagen Passat Variant and Santana (Germany), are extrusion blow moulded in high molecular weight polyethylene (Figure 2.12).

The same material and system of production is used in models produced by Ford, Citroen, Peugeot, Porsche and Renault in countries other than Europe. One exception is the tank for the Passat, produced by Volkswagen in South Africa, which is rotationally moulded in normal polyethylene (Section 2.14). Plastics fuel tanks for SAAB passenger cars are produced solely by Pyrkija Oy of Turku Finland. Other components include air inlet ducts and expansion tanks.

Recent developments in tank production have, among others, been directed towards eliminating fuel or gas permeation (as mentioned in Section 2.12). Methods have included various material treatments such as off-line, post moulding fluorination. Recently a breakthrough has been achieved by Krupp-Kautex with a coextrusion blow moulding process which, in conjunction with the company's blow moulding equipment (Figure 2.12) permits tanks to be produced with six layers. A barrier layer eliminates all diffusion and results in a tank which can pass all automotive manufacturers tests, including the tank being dropped from a height of 6m at a

Fig. 3.7 Recently developed multi-layer wall fuel tank. The unit, coextrusion blow moulded by Krupp Kautex, incorporates a barrier layer which virtually eliminates diffusion. (Courtesy Krupp Kautex)

temperature of −40°C. An example of one of the latest of these tanks is shown in Figure 3.7.

In many instances blow moulded tanks undergo secondary operations such as the hot-plate welding of elbow nipples and hose mountings to produce a complete tank (Figure 3.8). In some cases HDPE tanks can be blow moulded with an integral filler pipe

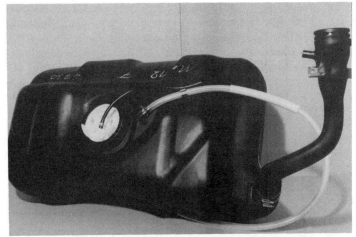

Fig. 3.8 A 60 litre blow moulded fuel tank for the Volkswagen Passat completely assembled with separately blow moulded filler. (Courtesy Krupp Kautex)

Fig. 3.9 *Fuel tanks in BASF Lupolen high density polyethylene are produced complete with integral filler. (Courtesy BASF)*

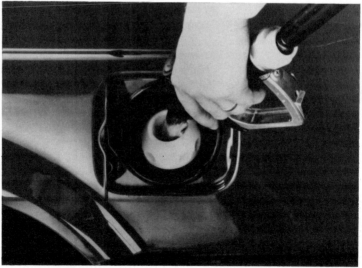

Fig. 3.10 *Non-return fuel filler system developed for BMW and Daimler-Benz models. The filler, designed to be thief-proof, is moulded in Delrin ST acetal homopolymer and Viton fluoroelastomer. (Courtesy Du Pont)*

(Figure 3.9). Additional and internal components such as the filling gauge and connections for the electrical rheostat and suction filter can be of acetal homopolymer, BASF's 'Ultradur' (PBT) and 'Ultraform' (POM), as they are resistant to modern fuels including methanol.

A recent development from W. Germany is a non-return filler system available for all current BMW and Daimler-Benz models. Moulded in Du Pont's Delrin ST acetal homopolymer and Viton fluoroelastomer, the device is designed to be theft-proof because once in place it cannot be removed without destroying the twist lock. Use of the filler also makes it impossible to put leaded petrol into cars designed to run on unleaded fuel because the opening is only of sufficient diameter to accept the nozzles of unleaded pumps (Figure 3.10).

3.5 COOLING SYSTEMS

Many automobile manufacturers have found that nylon cooling water pipes cost less to produce than metal pipes and can replace many of the intricately branched tubing made of a combination of metal and rubber. Cooling water circulation pipes in Opel's Kadett and Ascona models are of Durethan AKV 25H, a glass fibre reinforced nylon 66 from Bayer AG. Moulded by Marsbach of Germany, pipes come complete with integral fixing lugs and connecting sockets with the result that a whole series of individual components is reduced to just three parts (Figure 3.11). An interesting development in the cooling area is a double-grip hose clip designed to replace conventional metal worm-drive clips. Moulded as a one-piece unit in 'Maranyl' A 127 Blue 7229 heat stabilised injection grade, the corrosion-free clip is produced by Herbie Clips Ltd of Kidlington, England.

One of the earliest applications of plastics in the under-bonnet area were for cooling fans. Fans and shrouds can be injection moulded and offer excellent resistance to pitting from road debris and to oil and petrol fumes. A typical example is the fan and support on a Peugeot moulded in ICI's Maranyl GF nylon 66, shown in Figure 3.12. For some applications ICI's 'Verton' long fibre reinforced nylon and 'Procom' polypropylene compounds are specified. In addition to these materials ICI's Thermocomp compounds are specified for blow moulded radiator expansion tanks. Du Pont, ICI and other company's nylon grades are widely used for radiator end tanks. Rover radiator end tanks in Maranyl nylon GF 6.6 are shown in Figure 3.13. Daimler-Benz header tanks

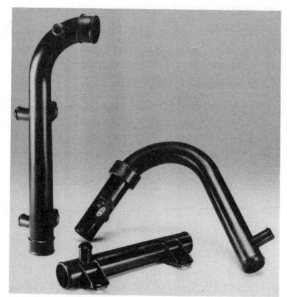

Fig. 3.11 Nylon 6.6 cooling water pipes in Bayer's Durethan glass-reinforced material are moulded complete with integral fixing lugs and connectors. (Courtesy Bayer)

Fig. 3.12 Fan and support on this model Peugeot are moulded in 'Maranyl' GF nylon 6.6. (Courtesy ICI)

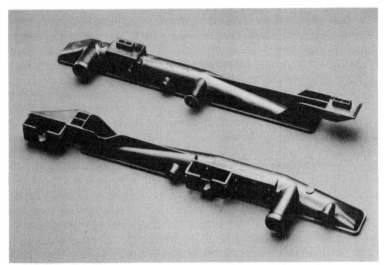

Fig. 3.13   Rover radiator end tank is produced in Maranyl GF 6.6 nylon. (Courtesy ICI)

moulded in BASF's 'Ultramid' 30% glass-filled nylon are shown in Figure 3.14.

The first application in Europe for a special high temperature hydrolysis-resistant type of Du Pont's 'Zytel' nylon resin is used in a new injection moulded radiator expansion tank for BMW cars. The unit which is mounted alongside the radiator saves space, weight and simplifies maintenance (Figure 3.15). The position and shape of the tank ensures that centrifugal forces when cornering will not disrupt coolant flow and permit the tank to operate satisfactorily with less fluid. The translucency of the polymer also helps to ensure the tank is filled to the correct level.

A 30% glass reinforced nylon by BIP Chemicals designated 'Beetle' AF 326 which offers good resistance to hydrolysis is also used to mould header and heater tanks for BMW and other international models. The material is not affected by ethylene glycol or other aromatics, is resistant to stress at high temperatures and meets the fire safety requirements of most European countries. In the USA, relocation of a radiator coolant reservoir to an under-bonnet area where the temperatures are some 14°C higher has demanded the use of a special grade of polyamide with the ability to withstand temperatures up to 135°C. The material, Capron 8270 from Allied Signal Engineered Plastics used for the blow moulded container is also unaffected by petrol, oil, grease, coolant chemicals and most solvents.

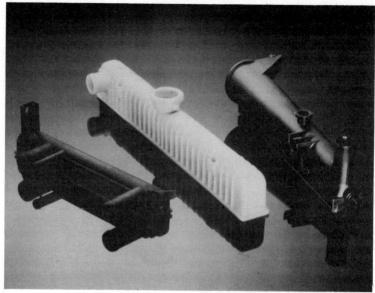

Fig. 3.14   Daimler-Benz radiator header tanks are moulded in BASF's 'Ultramid' 30% glass-filled nylon. (Courtesy BASF)

Fig. 3.15   High temperature, hydrolysis resistant Zytel is used for moulding radiator expansion tanks for BMW cars. (Courtesy Du Pont)

3.6 TRANSMISSIONS

As would be anticipated the transmission train relies to lesser extend on plastics than under-bonnet and bodywork areas and in the main provides seals and covers such as concertina type items on gear levers and oil retaining sleeves over universal joints.

A typical example of a blow moulded drive shaft guard in modified, pigmented LDPE UV stabilised, is produced in the USSR. Moulding is effected on a Battenfeld-Fischer type VK-10S automatic machine.

In some cases aramid fibres are replacing asbestos in clutch facings and brake pads. Kevlar, Du Pont's high strength para-aramid fibre provides a safer medium than asbestos in these applications and is also used increasingly in automatic clutch 'V' belts and in transmission oil cooler hose.

Recently considerable development has been taken by ICI Advanced Materials into plastics components that not only out perform their metal counterparts but also offer significant reductions in cost. An example of this work is the gear shift mechanism of the Audi 80 (Figure 3.16). By making the part which transfers movement of the gear lever to the rods operating the gearbox in Lubricomp RFL 4636 – a composite produced by LNP (a

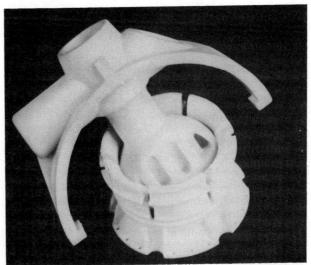

Fig. 3.16   Gear shift mechanism on Audi 80 is moulded in ICI's Lubricomp RFL 4636, a composite that provides inherent lubrication and good mechanical properties.
(Courtesy ICI)

part of ICI Advanced Materials), it provides inherent lubrication, good chemical resistance and excellent mechanical properties. The material has good moulding characteristics and by designing the complex component as two parts for snap-fit assembly it has virtually eliminated post moulding costs. Another application of engineering plastics in the transmission area is the 'J-gate' of the Jaguar Automatic XJ6. Designed to make it easier and more pleasant to drive the car in a sporting manner, the gate is laid out with 'Park-Reverse-Neutral-Drive' on the right so that when the driver is in 'Drive' he can move the lever across to a separate slot which selects 'Drive, 3 or 2, only. The component (Figure 3.17), is moulded in ICI's Verton RF 700-10 nylon with 50% long glass fibre reinforcement.

In the area of Formula One Grand Prix racing an early result of a partnership between ICI and Williams Engineering is the development of a gear selector made in APC 2 carbon fibre/PEEK composite which is able to withstand the hostile environment in the gearbox where oil temperature can reach 180°C. Other major developments being carried out by the partnership include a wheel,

Fig. 3.17   The gear change gate on the Jaguar Automatic XJ6, is designed to increase driving pleasure by regrouping of the gate positions. The component is moulded in Verton RF 700-10 nylon reinforced with glass fibre. (Courtesy ICI Advanced Materials)

Fig. 3.18   Engine cover in mineral-filled nylon on the Chrysler Eagle Premier in the United States. (Courtesy Monsanto Chemical Company, USA)

driveshaft and a diffuser panel. The latter component, located beneath the rear of the car, is a particularly demanding application due to the frictional wear involved.

In the United States, in particular, ambient temperatures can be extreme, thus any plastics material used in the engine bay must be capable of resisting both high and low temperatures. The engine cover used on the current model year Chrysler Eagle Premier (Figure 3.18) is moulded in Monsanto Chemical Company's Vydyne nylon, a 40% mineral-filled grade which provides heat resistance over 350°F coupled with excellent chemical resistance and appearance. For similar reasons associated with resistance to extremes of temperature, Monsanto's Vydyne Q958 mineral-filled nylon is used for the under-bonnet snow shield on the 1990 Ford Probe model (Figure 3.19).

Fig. 3.19 Monsanto's mineral-filled nylon Vydyne is used for this snow shield on the Ford Probe to prevent the accumulation of debris around the air duct, camshaft and throttle body. (Courtesy Monsanto Chemical Company, USA)

4
Chassis

4.1 SUSPENSIONS

Applications of plastics and plastics composites in the chassis include suspension and control systems, steering, the braking system, wheels and tyre (Figure 4.1). The almost universal use of coil springs in front suspensions has highlighted the application of thermoplastic elastomers, nylon mouldings with polychloroprene suspension rings and seals of fluorocarbon resin. Air suspension solenoid caps are of nylon with sleeves of synthetic rubber reinforced with high strength para-aramid fibre. MacPherson strut bellows are invariably of a thermoplastic elastomer as are front and rear anti-roll bar bushes and dust caps. The recent application of an engineering thermoplastic elastomer has been instrumental to the success of the patented suspension on the Jaguar XJ6 range. Moulded spring packers (Figure 4.2), are fitted top and bottom of each steel coil spring to separate the spring from the lower wishbone and the bodywork. The spring packers and locators are moulded in a variety of different thicknesses. Thus in combination the correct selection compensates for any imbalance between springs. 'Hytrel' thermoplastic elastomer was found in tests to withstand the heavy bump loads which in service would be severe for rubber compositions and would disintegrate glass-filled polypropylene packing discs. The spring packers have been evaluated by Jaguar on their development cars in North America, Australia and the Middle East.

Advances in the application of plastics in the leaf spring area includes the development of a suspension system incorporating fibre reinforcement, filament winding and resin transfer moulding techniques. The development of the cantilever type spring by a consortium which included Dowty Rotol, Ford, GKN, ICI, Shell and Volvo, demonstrates the potential of the glass fibre composite to combine the functions of springs, suspension arms and torsion members. A GKN Composites epoxy/glass suspension leaf spring computer, designed as a replacement for and to be interchangeable with steel leaf springs, is made from unidirectional glass fibre in

47

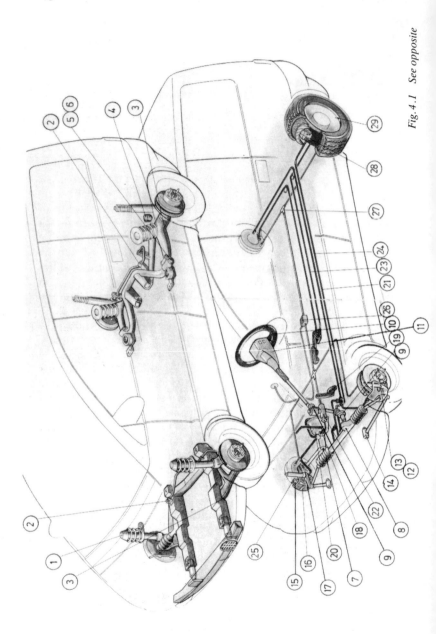

Fig. 4.1 See opposite

Fig. 4.1 The 'All Purpose' vehicle (APV), illustrates Du Pont's concept of the application of plastics in the chassis of a modern car.

1. Spring locators, air spring suspension, air shock sleeves, MacPherson strut bellows
2. Anti-roll bar bushes
3. Suspension bushes
4. Jounce bumpers
5. 'Solid state' strut suspension bushes
6. Suspension control circuits
7. Steering gear boots
8. Rack and pinion bushes, power steering reservoir, power steering hose
9. Steering column flexible coupling
10. Steering wheel, steering wheel tilt bushes
11. Steering column shield
12. Bearing linings
13. Ball caps and ball joint seals
14. Tie rod ends
15. Brake lining, pad reinforcement, wear sensor
16. Disc brake shield, caliper bellows
17. Brake boots
18. Brake tubing
19. Brake pedal pad
20. Brake valve servo
21. Brake hose
22. Brake fluid reservoir
23. Handbrake cable cover
24. Brake fluid line protection
25. ABS sensors using optical fibre encoder
26. ABS flexible circuitry
27. ABS interconnectors
28. Tyre belting
29. Tyre valves and low pressure indicators

Shell Chemicals UK Epicote epoxy resin matrix. Advantages of the spring are primarily its low weight which is said to be about half that of the equivalent taper leaf spring and some third of the weight of a multi-leaf spring.

One of the major problems associated with composite springs is attachment. Holes weaken the component, the composite material is not readily compatible with adhesives and thermosetting based materials cannot be welded. In the new spring the problem is

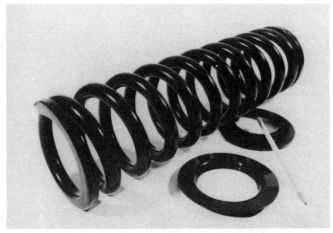

4.2 Thermoplastic elastomer spring packers used in the front suspension of the Jaguar XJ6 range of cars compensate for imbalance between springs. (Courtesy Du Pont)

overcome by the incorporation of standard and replaceable bushes at each end. A central pad provides a location on the axle. Originally a composite of carbon and glass fibres in epoxy resin was used. Later it was discovered that the carbon fibres were not only too expensive but were unnecessary; the glass alone provided good fatigue properties, wear resistance, resistance to chemical corrosion and gave excellent design flexibility.

4.2   STEERING: FLEXIBLE COUPLINGS AND COMPOSITE STEERING WHEELS

Ethylene acrylic rubbers and engineering thermoplastic elastomers are replacing natural rubbers in many areas of the steering gear. Notable applications are steering gear boots and steering column flexible couplings. High strength acetal resins are widely used in rack-and-pinion bushings, power steering reservoirs and in steering gear joints. Tie-rod ends benefit from coatings of non-stick, low coefficient of friction fluorocarbon resins with caps of polychloroprene synthetic rubber. A current investigation into steering wheel design is the use of a moulded core of glass reinforced nylon with a skin of melt processible rubber.

4.3   BRAKING SYSTEMS

One of the more significant developments in the interests of safety in the chassis area have been in the replacement of asbestos in brake linings and pad reinforcement, associated with modern high efficiency systems, with high strength para-aramid fibre. In the brake assembly, where conditions of fluctuating temperature coupled with flexing and the need to resist aggressive fluids and dust from brake pads are critical, nylon mouldings, sometimes reinforced with glass fibre, serve as disc brake shields. Ethylene acrylic rubber is used for caliper bellows and for brake actuating tubing. Brake boots are invariably of polychloroprene synthetic rubber with brake pad wear sensors of fluorocarbon resin. Brake hoses are also of fluorocarbon resin, hydrocarbon rubber or polychloroprene synthetic rubber reinforced with aramid fibres. Brake fluid lines to both front and rear assemblies are protected in the Du Pont system by a coating of Tedlar PVF. Sensors in ABS systems use optical fibre encoders, flexible circuitry incorporating polyamide film and Du Pont connectors.

Recent advances in reinforced thermoplastics are highlighted by the development of, for example, a glass mat reinforced material by BASF Elastogran Kunstoff Technik, via a melt extrusion technique with subsequent calendering. The material is based predominately on polypropylene and can be press moulded to produce strong, impact resistant parts suitable for use in the automotive industry. Applications can include engine compartment guards, seat parts and bumper beams. One sophisticated application is in the pedal box of the Peugeot 405. The application of the material permits off-line assembly of the brake and clutch pedal box complete with the brake servo. Another critical application of a high strength, reinforced material is in the Ferrari 408, four-wheel drive sports car. Here the material chosen for the accelerator, clutch and brake pedals is ICI's Verton RF 700-10EM, a 50% long glass fibre reinforced nylon. The brake pedal, moulded by Fratelli Cattini in Italy, was specified to withstand 500,000 cycles with loads varying from 100 to 900kg. Drivers of the high speed car will be relieved to know that at one million cycles no signs of fatigue were apparent and this test was abandoned. In load-to-break tests Ferrari demanded no fracture at 1500N. The pedal broke only when a load of 6000N was applied. The material also met the deflection-under-load requirements at temperatures ranging from −20°C to +80°C.

4.4   ROAD WHEELS: WEIGHT SAVING AND COMPOSITES

The replacement of pressed steel and aluminium by plastics for automobile wheels holds a number of attractions both from the point of view of production and savings in unsprung weight. Initial work aimed at evaluating the feasibility of using a moulded wheel has been carried out by Bayer in conjunction with a major manufacturer of motor cycle wheels. The work so far has included the all-in-one injection of moulded nylon wheels in both 30% and 50% glass fibre reinforced Durathan B. Tests which simulated extremes of conditions that were far in excess of what a motor cycle wheel would be likely to encounter indicated the possibilities of applying the technique to automobile wheels.

Indeed in the US, limited edition, high performance models based on Chrysler's Dodge Shadow will be fitted with all-plastics wheels moulded in vinyl ester sheet moulding compound. The material, Fibreride, developed by Lancing Motor Wheel Corporation of Michigan, is based on Derakane 790 vinyl ester from Dow Chemical. For wheel construction, the composite incorporates continuous glass fibres arranged in an 'X' pattern. The first production run of some 500 wheels moulded by Goodyear Tire and Rubber Company are to be used by Shelby Automobiles of California in cars designated Shelby CSX. The composite wheel offers a 10% to 15% weight saving as compared with cast aluminium and some 30% to 45% as compared with a mild steel wheel. Other advantages are said to be freedom from corrosion, better dimensional uniformity from wheel-to-wheel and run-out characteristics superior to steel wheels.

4.5 ROAD WHEEL TRIM

With the introduction of 'full-face' wheel trims such as used on the Renault 21 (Figure 4.3), large volume automobile manufacturers recognised the advantages of replacing metal with a nylon that was tough, non-corrosive and both chemical and temperature resistant. Additionally, because the material could be injection moulded without difficulty it permitted greater design freedom and allowed manufacturers to produce wheel trims that were not only aerodynamic in form but also could easily be altered in appearance to differentiate between models. Further more the injection process allowed the manufacturer to incorporate its logo in the design and to paint the trim in accordance with the colour of each model.

Plastics processors such as, for example, Wegu, with plants in

Fig. 4.3 'Full-face' wheel covers on the Renault 21 are moulded in nylon 66. (Courtesy Du Pont)

Germany and Canada, work in conjunction with raw material suppliers to develop various designs of wheel trim for manufacturers, such as BMW, Ford, Daimler-Benz and Volkswagen. Materials include two grades of ICI's Maranyl TB-570, a 30% glass fibre reinforced and mineral impact modified nylon 6 and TA-515, a 30% mineral impact modified nylon 66.

European automobile manufacturers who have chosen to use engineering thermoplastic wheel covers because of their improved physical properties, particularly in the areas of heat, impact and corrosion resistance, include Renault who use Du Pont's Minlon 30% high impact strength, modified nylon 66 in the 25TS, GTS and Espace models. Other applications of plastics wheel trims have included decorative, painted caps of Ultramid KR-4652, a BASF copolyamide 66/6 created for the Golf models. The material reinforced with mineral filler has isotropic and reduced shrinkage characteristics and is suitable for painting on large scale production runs. The cap (Figure 4.4), is fixed to the ventilation slots of the wheel rim and incorporates a valve flap also of Ultramid KR-4652 integrated into the outer edge of the hub cap.

A new lightweight wheel system designed by Autotechnik Geiger of Germany to improve wheel aesthetics by completely masking and retaining the balance weights employs a rim ring of Du Pont's Minlon thermoplastic resin. The rim (Figure 4.5) contains no metal reinforcement but, due to the stability of the mineral reinforced and

Fig. 4.4   Decorative, painted wheel caps in copolymer are used on Volkswagen Golf and Jetta models. (Courtesy BASF)

*Fig. 4.5   A lightweight wheel trim in mineral reinforced and toughened nylon 66
designed to retain and mask the balance weights, can be retro fitted to certain Mercedes
and BMW models. (Courtesy Du Pont)*

toughened nylon 66, stays in place even under extreme driving
conditions and when heated by high speed braking. The system
designated as the 'BST' wheel has the Federal German Vehicle
Authority's roadworthiness permit and is available in the 7-1/25 ×
15 size as a retrofit accessory for Mercedes W201 and W124 models
and for BMW's new 7/iE32 and 5/1E34 models.

Considerable interest is also currently being shown by a number
of automobile manufacturers in special finishes for roadwheels.
One system used by MacPherson Industrial Coatings on cast
aluminium wheels made by the Eurocast Division of Parkfield
Wheels in the UK for the new Ford Fiesta consists of applying and
stoving a base coat of polyester followed by a one-component
polyurethane coating which is dried at room temperature. The
process is finalised by the application of a two-component acrylic
urethane coating stoved at 80°C. The system is said to be applicable
to polymeric wheels with minimum modification.

4.6   BUMPERS: DESIGN, WEIGHT SAVING, SPECIAL MODELS

One area of automotive engineering in which the application of
plastics materials has probably affected development to a greater
extent than any other is in the design of bumpers. The current trend

to integrate bumpers and front air dams into bodywork raises the question of whether bumpers should be discussed under the title 'chassis' or 'bodywork'. In view of the fact that bumpers proper are mounted on the chassis, some notes on their development in the context of plastics usage are included here.

The primary purpose of bumpers is to protect the body and adjacent parts such as the radiator and lamps from minor collisions. Early specifications demanded that the bumper should be capable of withstanding frontal impact with a stationary obstacle at a speed of 4km without damage. Additionally, the material of construction must ensure long life, have good corrosion resistance and be unaffected by changes in temperature and humidity. As an energy absorber three design strategies are applicable; to place the energy absorbing element ahead or behind the mountings or to use a flexible medium without an energy absorber.

Early attempts to reduce parking lot damage in the US consisted of a layer of dense, resiliant urethane foam moulded on to a metal mounting. Later US legislation on low impact damage led to the first use of polyurethanes, initially as an easily formed skin of RIM elastomer to cover a hydraulic ram. Advances were rapid, particularly in the area of full 'facias' or front-end. This technique gave greater design freedom since quite simple changes in the shape of the frontal area allowed differentiation between models.

In Europe early designs were similar in approach but to reduce weight the foam was cored out to produce a series of energy absorbing ribs. The system was used on certain early Ford Capri, MG and Volkswagen models. Other early designs took the plastic bumper a stage further by spraying and baking it in-line to match the body colour. One material developed by Bayer for this purpose was Pocan S-1506, an elastomer modified polybutylene terephthalate thermoplastic polyester which possessed the advantage of allowing the bumper to be processed through the body paint line at temperatures of up to 140°C.

Since the Metro was first launched in 1980 the latest generation of ICI advanced materials has played a significant part in the evolution of the new Rover Metro launched in May 1990. Improvements in plastics materials and moulding techniques have encouraged designers to adopt all-embracing bumper designs. Various integral features such as spoilers, air intakes and foglamp housings, deep enough to form almost the entire nose section of a small car or a large part of the tail area are possible.

The new Metro has a deep, moulded bumper/spoiler section at the front and a smaller but still substantial bumper moulding at the rear. The choice of material was aided by the long established working relationship between Rover and ICI. Both companies were anxious to exploit the latest material developments especially the 'controlled rheology' of Propathane and Procom polypropylene grades with their high impact strength and low melt temperature making them most suitable for the production of large, distortion-free mouldings.

The technical requirements for the bumpers were considerable. The front unit is four times the size of the original and apart from being aesthetically acceptable, the new bumpers were required to provide a substantial measure of 'zero damage' protection against low-speed impacts of up to 2.5km/h. The material specified for both front and rear units were a controlled rheology grade of Propathane and Procam X5S753, an elastomer modified polypropylene. Moulds for the units were produced by Tooling Products (Langrish) Ltd with mouldings by Sterling Engineering Products (Figure 4.6).

These and other developments in bumper design coupled with

Fig. 4.6   Bumpers for the Rover 800 models are moulded in a grade of elastomer modified polypropylene by Sterling Engineering Products. Moulds are by Tooling Products (Langrish) Ltd.

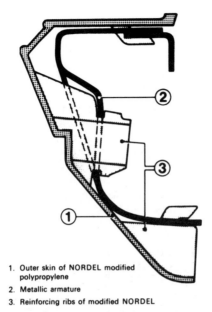

1. Outer skin of NORDEL modified
   polypropylene
2. Metallic armature
3. Reinforcing ribs of modified NORDEL

*Fig. 4.7   Bumper construction on some Volkswagen models consists of a cover of
hydrocarbon rubber mounted on a metal backing to absorb greater impact forces: (1)
outer skin of modified polypropylene, (2) metal armature, (3) reinforcing ribs of
modified polypropylene. (Courtesy Du Pont)*

advances in materials have demonstrated that the energy
absorption properties of, for example, the polyurethanes allow the
earlier heavy, hydraulic systems to be replaced by simpler box
sections. In this context developments by ICI have produced a
special high performance, semi-rigid polyurethane foam system
which can be securely bonded to a Procom polypropylene
compound by means of a special primer to produce a composite
construction with the required degree of rigidity and energy
absorption over a wide temperature range. An advantage of the
technique is that since the bumper does not spring apart on impact
the shock is distributed over a wide area. Deflection of the bonded
bumper has been shown to be only 20% of the deflection of an
unbonded component. In this way it is possible to mount the front
unit closer to the radiator and thus make the overall length of the car
shorter.

In another approach, bumper covers of Du Pont's Nordel
hydrocarbon rubber are mounted on a metal backing (Figure 4.7)
which serves as a structural member to absorb greater collision
forces. The unit consists of a substantial surface skin backed by

moulded ribs that reinforce the material and assist in distributing impact over the entire elastomeric surface. In a moderate speed collision in which the metal members supporting the elastomer are slightly bent, deformation is hidden and need not be repaired. Initially introduced on the Volkswagen Passat and Sirocco models, the bumpers are standard on the Golf.

Polypropylene bumpers for the Rover 200 range are among high production rate items in the UK. Some 400 car sets are produced on a 'just-in time' (JIT) basis each week by Caroden Rolinx using a hot-runner injection moulding system on two Klockner Windsor machines. Second operations on the basic mouldings include heat-staking of attachment points. The Discovery, Rover's latest off-the-road vehicle, is fitted with polyurethane RRIM, 15% glass fibre reinforced bumpers developed in conjunction with Holden Hydroman as a high specification component capable of matching the vehicle's rugged performance.

In the US, high production rates of automobiles has encouraged the use of sophisticated bumper manufacturing techniques such as the Cincinnati-Milacron RIM 125 line at Diamond Star Motors, Illinois plant which produces more than 500,000 front and rear fascias annually for the Plymouth Laser and Mitsubishi Eclipse models. In view of the high production rates required, the machines feature rollers in the lower platens and specially designed mould clamps to facilitate rapid mould changes. Moulds are transported automatically from mould store to machine. The line also features liquid-monomer bulk handling, automatic glass fibre reinforcement/plastic blending and recirculation and conditioning units. Another example of American high rate technology for bumper production is the eight-station system, developed by Wilson Automation of Warren, Michigan, for applying adhesive and ultrasonically bonding reinforcements into bumpers at rates of up to 85 parts/hour.

Limited production models

While compounds of polypropylene and olefinic rubbers, polycarbonate/polybutyl terephthalate, polyurethane RIM and RRIM systems all find their place in bumpers, providing high hysteresis and delayed elasticity coupled with economically viable production techniques, there are instances in which for styling and production reasons different materials and technologies must be applied. Examples include the bumper on the Ferrari Testrossa. This limited production item well illustrates the problems facing the Pininfarina designers in choosing the most suitable technology. The choice was between producing a bumper in glass reinforced polyester in a carbon mould or with the cost of a RIM item made in a polished steel mould. The conclusion was that a quantity production system producing finished parts ready for painting was not economically viable for production runs of less than one thousand per year. An additional problem was that external shape changes would probably be required after a year or so thus bringing mould depreciation costs into consideration. Secondly, the design and profile of the bumper excluded the use of low-stiffness materials or considerable deformation in the event of an impact; it was, therefore, designed as three elements consisting of an outer shell of rigid GRP with an inserted steel bar and two elastomeric impact absorbing elements between the bumpers and the bodywork.

In production, uni and bi-directional lamination of GRP is carried out in a female mould with concurrent insertion of the steel bar and mounting brackets. Final operations are curing at ambient pressure followed by surface preparation, priming and painting. For the larger production runs of the Ferrari V-8 engined Mondial 2+2 model, bumpers are manufactured from polyurethane using reaction injection techniques by Macchi Arturo at its Renate plant near Milan. The materials are produced by ICI's Italian subsidiary Atlas Europol.

Front and rear fascias on the Porsche Carrera 4 incorporate 'Bexloy', Du Pont's thermoplastic engineering resin, over reinforced reaction injection moulded polyurethane. The front fascia consists of a large moulding (Figure 4.8(a)), and two half-covers or valances. The large moulding which is painted in body colour off-line, includes a face bar, licence plate, blinker lamp, fog lamp housings and an intake grille. The two valances below are unpainted and are designed to reduce drag. The rear fascia (Figure 4.8(b)) consists of three sections, a mid-section painted in body colour and incorporating the licence plate pocket and illumination and wrap-arounds for each side of the car. Together the front and rear fascias six components weigh a total of 10.9kg. Reportedly the use of Bexloy V in this application facilitates a simple painting operation after moulding as it eliminates post-finishing operations usually required to achieve a class 'A' surface when RRIM material is used.

Ford Sierra Ghia bumper trims are of a design which, at the front, incorporate overriders and enlarged cut-outs for fog-lights. While the standard Sierra bumper has an inset trimstrip, the more complex Ghia moulding is enhanced with a moulding in ICI polyurethane which runs beneath the headlamps and round to the

Fig. 4.8   (a) Front and (b) rear fascias of the Porsche Carrera 4 consist of a skin of thermoplastic engineering resin over a RRIM injection moulded polyurethane core. (Courtesy DuPont)

front wheel arches. The most powerful versions of the Audi 90 and Coupe (136 h.p. and above), are fitted with front bumpers (Figure 4.9), of Pocan from Bayer which offers high impact strength, high heat resistance and excellent dimensional stability. Bumpers are easy to paint and exceptionally resistant to fuels, de-icing salt and

Fig. 4.9   The Audi 90 and Coupe are fitted with front bumpers of Pocan S 7913, a PBT/PC blend by Bayer AG.

other chemicals. The self-supporting bumper structure consists of a beam to which the bumper shell with its integrated spoiler is welded. The flowability of this grade is a decisive factor in the economic injection moulding of such large parts produced by Peguform-Werke, Neustadt/Donau, Germany. Subsequent two-colour painting in black and body colour, using two-pack polyurethane coatings, presents no problems. The bumper system effectively prevents minor damage resulting from low speed knocks (4km/h) and conforms with European guidelines.

Cars including specialist models intended for export to the US are required to fulfil US regulations regarding the ability to withstand an 8km/hour impact. In the case of the Aston Martin Lagonda as with other small volume production models, it is uneconomic to invest in expensive metal press tools and dies. In the case of the Aston Martin the bumper units designed to have a subtle shape and a high quality black finish. They consist of a RIM polyurethane outer skin covering a foam filling which, in turn, is formed over an aluminium armature. The skins are moulded by Holden Hydroman and are finished with a polyurethane paint by Aston Martin.

5
Bodywork

5.1 APPLICATION OF PLASTICS – EARLY WORK

In reviewing the application of plastics in the construction of bodywork it will be appreciated that early production models such as the General Motors Corvette in the United States, the Matra Bagheera in France, Reliant Robin and Scimitar, the TVR Taimar and the Lotus cars range of sports cars in the United Kingdom have involved the use of glass fibre reinforced polyester resin. Although these models have been produced in modest quantities compared with conventional steel bodied cars they have performed well in service and due largely to their resistance to corrosion and in some cases to good power to weight characteristics, have retained their second hand value significantly better than models produced by traditional means. In addition to these limited quantity productions there have been many models built by hand layup methods (Section 2.16). These have included work by individuals and companies specialising in the production of replicas of classic sports cars of past years.

Since the introduction of glass fibre reinforced polyester materials (GRP), material manufacturers and automobile manufacturers have been active in examining the application of other thermosets and thermoplastics and in particular the use of composites for large scale bodywork. Results from the building of prototype vehicles has led to optimism and market studies have subscribed to the view that the principle area of greatest growth will be in secondary vehicle body components. This view is however being challenged by material and processing developments that tend to discount the argument that barriers to the use of plastics in primary structures are current investment in steel press lines, lack of the necessary stiffness of plastics materials and speed of production. Recycling of the resultant plastics scrap is accepted as a problem but is one which is currently being addressed both in Europe and in the United States (Chapter 6). Another problem which is receiving attention is associated with the in-line painting of bodywork. Reportedly, Bayer take the view that despite the developments

63

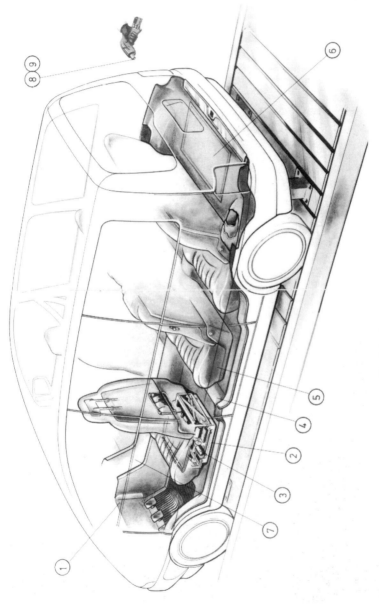

Fig. 5.1 See page 67

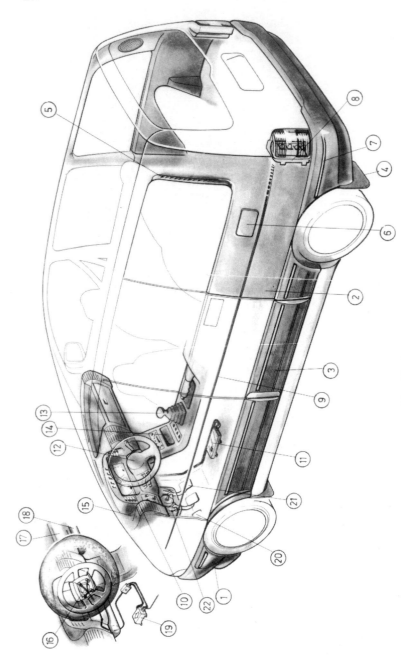

Fig. 5.2   See page 67

65

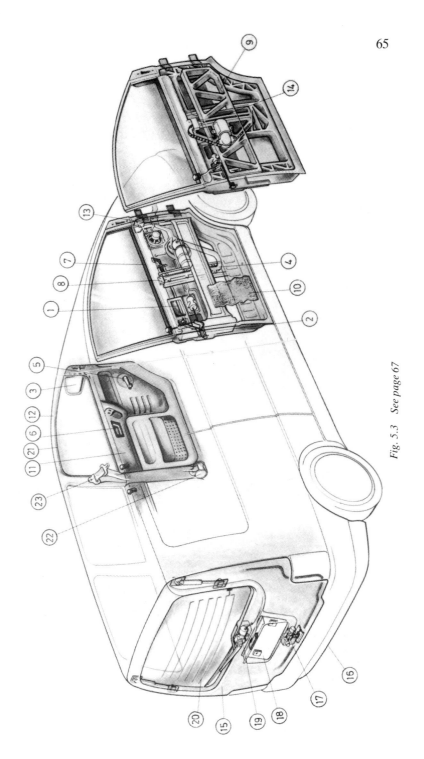

Fig. 5.3   See page 67

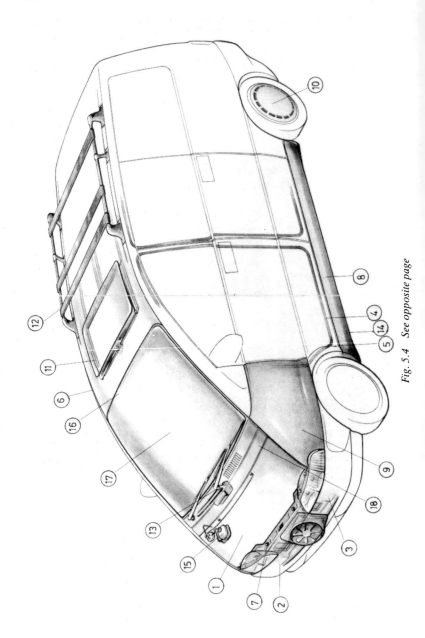

Fig. 5.4 See opposite page

BODYWORK

67

Fig. 5.1 The 'All-Purpose' vehicle (APV) illustrates Du Pont's concept of the application of plastics for bodywork and trim in the modern car. (Courtesy Du Pont)
1. Acoustical barrier
2. Seat frame, suspension and lock components
3. Electric thrust pads and motor housings
4. Floor coverings and carpet backing
5. Upholstery and trim
6. Exhaust heat shields
7. Air conditioning components
8. and 9. Special finishes

Fig. 5.2 The APV. (Courtesy Du Pont)

1. Air dam and bumper fascia
2. Body panels and quarter panels
3. Side mouldings and rubbing strips
4. Mudflaps
5. C-column grille
6. Fuel tank flap
7. Bright trim
8. Rear lamp retainer panel and lamp seals
9. Decals
10. Instrument cluster circuit, display housing, speedometer gears
11. Navigation and information systems, printer circuit boards etc.
12. Steering wheel skin, steering column switch assembly
13. Gear lever and boot
14. Ashtray
15. Dashboard skin
16. Airbag deployment doors
17. Crash pads
18. Knee bolster
19. Collision warning system
20. Clutch pedal
21. Accelerator pedal, pad and bearing
22. Pedal box

Fig. 5.3 The APV. (Courtesy Du Pont)

1. Exterior door handles and backing plates
2. Door lock housings
3. External mirror housing
4. Window regulator system
5. Window winder
6. Interior door handles
7. Window seals
8. Window lift stops
9. Intrusion seal
10. Door trim
11. Door upholstery
12. Door seals
13. Multiplex systems
14. Door cassette
15. Boot lid
16. Rear panels
17. Boot lock housing
18. Licence holder
19. Rear window wiper seal
20. Window demister conductors
21. Passive restraint system
22. Seat retractor and buckle
23. B and C pillar loop overmoulding

Fig. 5.4 The APV. (Courtesy Du Pont)

1. Bonnet
2. Bumper fascia, ventilator grilles, bumper beams, bumper management unit
3. Bumper mounts
4. Threshold seals
5. Body plugs
6. Roof seals
7. Adjustable bonnet stop
8. Door sills, (rocker panels)
9. Front quarter panel
10. Wheel covers and hub caps
11. Sunroof frame
12. Luggage rack parts
13. Wiper drive system
14. Lift jack support
15. Windscreen washer reservoir cap and fluid heater
16. Sunvisor support
17. Safety glass
18. Crash pads and crash pad skin

currently taking place, the real breakthrough for external body panels will not come until there are paint lines that permit flexible coating systems to be used at stoving temperatures below 120°C. (Figures 5.1 to 5.4 indicate the many applications of plastics in bodywork.)

5.2 COMPOSITE CONSTRUCTION

While currently the 'all plastic' body remains confined to prototypes and experimental work, a number of highly successful road models are produced using a composite of metal frame and GRP panels. Examples include the Kitten and Scimitar sports saloon produced in modest numbers by Reliant in the United Kingdom. The highly successful Lotus range of high speed sports cars (Figure 5.5) incorporate only a rigid tubular chassis upon which is mounted a completely glass fibre reinforced body produced by a resin transfer process. Bodies are produced by a two-piece moulding, an upper and a lower half, which are assembled with an horizontal joint along the waistline. This would appear to permit the use of, for example, three moulds, one lower and two upper to produce two body styles. The method of producing a paint finish by spraying the mould with a polyurethane paint system prior to applying the gel coat is said to be unique at the present time on a production line. Other UK

Fig. 5.5   The Lotus Elite features a glass fibre reinforced polyester resin body moulded by a resin transfer process. (Courtesy Lotus Cars Ltd)

manufacturers of successful sports models include TVR Engineering who match a GRP body to a stove enamelled steel chassis and West Winds, producers of the Lima range of two-seat sports cars, who also use an extremely rigid chassis matched with a completely unstressed GRP body. In France the Matra Simca 'Bagheera' demonstrates the application of a resin injection process for the production of body panels in conjunction with a rigid chassis. The Alpine Renault and the Talbot Murena are also French examples of a combination of steel and GRP external bodywork. In the Murena panels are carried on a steel supporting cage with auxiliary framing, whilst the Alpine Renault incorporates a central chassis with a rollover safety bar.

The Renault Espace, one of the most original shapes to appear on the European automobile scheme in 1984, is termed by Renault 'a one-box sedan' a vehicle the shape of which is completely integrated so there is no separate bonnet or obvious rear luggage compartment. The form offers a drag coefficient of 0.32 which is better than most contemporary sedans. To eliminate corrosion the company's designers together with their opposite numbers at Matra use a zinc galvanized steel skeleton frame completely clothed with plastics panels. The outer body panels are mainly of glass-filled polyester either injected or compression moulded in a similar manner to the rear hatch and bonnet of the Citroen BX.

German manufacturers Mercedes Benz and BMW, as would be anticipated, are both active in the bodywork development area. The latter company who have produced the Mach 1 model in limited numbers use a tubular frame to support external GRP bodywork. A somewhat similar system was introduced by Ferrari for its earlier GT4 high-speed coupe. In the United States the still much sought after Corvette range incorporates a rigid box frame to support its plastics bodywork. Originally production was confined to wet-layup GRP moulding but later production was converted to the use of low profile SMC for the bodywork. The Corvette range still represents the largest production of a plastics bodied car, the success of which has highlighted the suitability of SMC for bodywork. Significantly, European market studies indicate that sheet moulding compounds are poised for some 15% growth over the next five years. Currently SMC accounts for over 20% of all thermoset compounds, a market estimated to have reached some 170,000 tons in 1988. A significant advance in the usage of SMC is the introduction by General Motors in the United States of its GM-200 luxury 'Peoples carrier' which is badged variously as the Chevrolet 'Lumina' and Oldsmobile 'Silhouette'. The vehicle which uses plastics panels on an aluminium frame is intended for a production of up to 225,000 units/year.

5.3   BODY COMPONENTS: COMPOSITE ASSEMBLIES, DOORS AND TAILGATES

Of the many applications of plastics for secondary bodywork, limitations of space permit the highlighting of only a selection of examples. The Billion ZMC injection technology (Section 2.7), first used on the Citroen BX range for the production of bonnets and tailgates, is widely used by other manufacturers and is currently applied on the production line of the Citroen AX 'Super Mini'. The injection of long glass fibre reinforced polyester at conventional production rates has also made the process applicable to a wide range of secondary body components.

One of the most significant developments alongside the various advances in the design and the use of composite materials for bumper production, is the introduction of replaceable items such as wings, side 'rocker' panels (Figure 5.6) and 'soft' front and rear ends designed to increase safety, reduce low impact damage and save weight. Current examples include the use of Dow's Spectrim RD 403 RIM system by Marley Foam for the off-line painted 'rocker' panels on each side of the Ford Sapphire RS Cosworth. The material incorporates a mould release agent and is reinforced with 15% of hammer milled glass to improve dimensional stability.

Fig. 5.6   Glass fibre reinforced rocker panels in Desmopan polyurethane elastomer. (Courtesy Bayer AG)

BMW also use Dow's Spectrim RD RIM for the bumper cover, front spoiler and rear fascia on its Series 3 cars. Parts moulded by Pfeba in Germany are painted with a flexible high gloss PU finish. They weigh 2.7, 2.8 and 5.5 kg respectively. Since its acquisition of Seger & Hoffman AG, now an integral part of the Dow Automobile Development Centre in Fagerwilen, Switzerland, the company have specialised in advanced composites and resin and fibre technology.

A major area of development is in resin transfer moulding (RTM) (Section 2.16) which can exhibit a class 'A' finish direct from the mould and may require only one coat of paint. Projects have included body shell components for the BMW M1 and Audi Quattro. Currently the company supply BMW with boot lids, storage cover and hood for the prestige Z1 roadster.

In the United States stainless steel body side components on the 1989 Pontiac 'Grand Am' and Oldsmobile 'Calais' are replaced by mouldings in 'Polypur' FPU-1103 thermoplastic polyurethane developed by A. Shulman, Akron, Ohio and moulded by General Motor's Fisher Guide plant in Syracuse. Based on Dow Chemical's 'Pellethane' thermoplastic polyurethane elastomers, Polypur offers rigidity, dimensional stability, a low coefficient of expansion and a non-primed paintability – parts of up to 7 feet can be moulded with a single gating and without weld lines.

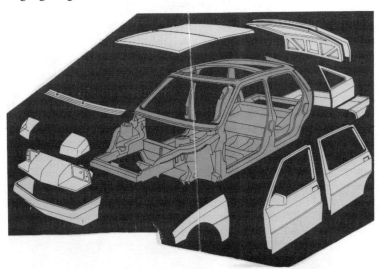

Fig. 5.7   Bumper mouldings, doors and exterior panels in General Electric Plastics materials feature in the company's concept of the use of plastics in conjunction with a rigid metal frame. (Courtesy General Electric Plastics)

Bumper mouldings with integrated spoiler and air intake, lateral and rocker panels designed to resist low speed impacts and stone chipping, fenders and door mouldings, all feature materials by General Electric Plastics Europe (Figure 5.7) in its concept for the application of exterior body components. The all plastic door concept (Figure 5.8) consists of a two-piece injection moulding, the inner member of which integrates fixing points for interior trim items and provides the arm rest and map pocket. The moulding can be ribbed as necessary for additional rigidity. The outer member is a single skin to give the exterior styling form and to offer dent and corrosion resistance. The construction is claimed to offer a weight saving of some 20kg on a four-door vehicle as compared with a conventional steel assembly. The company's proposed design of tailgate also features two injection mouldings, the inner being of ribbed construction with all hardware mounting points integrated. Simple steel pressings give reinforcement in hinge and lock areas. The outer member, a single skin of 2.5mm wall thickness closes the construction which, combined with bonded glazing, provides a torsionally stable, lightweight, rigid assembly. Various materials are used including Noryl, PPO/DA GTX alloy, Valox and Zenoy thermoplastics resins and Ultem polyethermide resins.

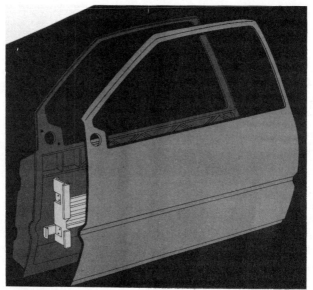

Fig. 5.8   General Electric Plastics concept of an 'all-plastics' door produced as a two-piece injection moulding. (Courtesy General Electric Plastics)

The roof concept, moulded in one-piece with the rear area painted in body, colour, incorporates the in-moulded rear spoiler. Impax sheet, a new family of thermoplastics sheet materials developed by General Electric Plastics based on polymeric blends is used increasingly for both interior and exterior body components. In the 'City car' manufactured by Aixam in France, the floor pan and engine compartment are thermoformed from Impax sheet. Other applications are seat shells, interior cladding and dashboards. Exterior uses include fenders and bumper or wheel arch extenders.

Developments by Du Pont for the production of doors has led the company to specify thermoplastic polyester (PET) which is able to withstand paint oven temperatures. The structure was designed to use two forms of glass reinforcement. For the main structural elements a continuous unidirectional pre-coated glass fibre at 50% by volume is used. For the panel an isotropic sheet incorporating 25mm long fibres at 50% by volume was specified. The materials were combined in a pre-form for compression moulding. The aim was a 60 second cycle, a target already achieved for wing and exterior door panels. The process consists of three stages. Firstly, the preform is heated to the melt temperature of the PET and is then transferred to the mould cavity and compressed. The mould is maintained at a lower temperature than the preform so solidification is rapid. The door is then transferred to a tempering chamber to undergo controlled cooling to develop the optimum properties of the material.

5.4   EXTERNAL SAFETY: ACTIVE AND PASSIVE SAFETY, DAMAGE LIMITATION

The increasing volume of traffic, the rise in the number of accidents coupled with soaring repair costs are the main reasons why the subject of safety in automobiles has become a matter of great concern to designers both in Europe and the United States. In this area a distinction is made between active and passive safety. The term 'Active safety' refers to the control of factors which prevent road accidents: good tyres and brakes, good all-round visibility and conspicuous colours. 'Passive safety' is intended to prevent or limit damage should an accident occur. It includes protective cushioning, safety belts and head restraints in the car's interior (Figure 5.9).'External safety' on the other hand, can be provided by certain sections of the bodywork that deform in the event of an accident to lessen the impact on the occupants. Applications take a number of

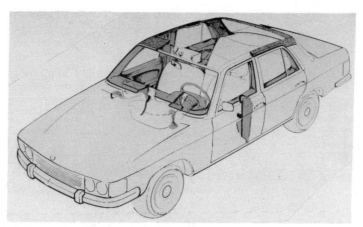

*Fig. 5.9   'Passive safety' measures designed to limit damage in the event of an accident
include cushioning, safety belts and head restraints*

forms in addition to sections designed solely for damage limitation, and include cost saving and styling exercises. One example of such an application is provided by the Alfa Romeo GTV6 (Figure 5.10) which, in addition to using a front bumper and spoiler in RIM polyurethane, incorporates sill panels in the material as a section of the bonnet to provide extra clearance above the induction system. The moulding is inserted in a cut-out in the bonnet panel. The

Fig. 5.10   Alfa Romeo bumpers and sill panels. (Courtesy ICI)

Fig. 5.11   MG Metro Turbo wheel arch extensions and spoilers. (Courtesy ICI)

alternative to this solution of providing extra space would be a very expensive press tool for a relatively low volume pressing.

Another example of the application of RIM moulded polyurethane is in the styling of the MG Metro Turbo. Here the rear spoiler consists of a glass reinforced moulding which is added to the standard body shell. With the car's high performance and the need for wider tyres, the wing arches are extended by 'eyebrow' RIM mouldings of glass-filled polyurethane as are the air inlets for front disc-brake cooling (Figure 5.11).

5.5   'SOFT ENDS': PHYSICAL REQUIREMENTS, DEFORMATION AND MATERIALS

For a long time the concept of a 'soft face' on bodywork was thought to be impracticable because no material existed that was capable of meeting the demands of such an external component. To meet these demands bodywork sections of approximately 3-4mm would be required to be flexible, to have powers of recovery, not to fracture at low temperatures but provide stiffness at temperatures that could be expected on the road. Additionally these should not sag or transmit any noise resulting from vibration and, importantly should be capable of being painted in body colour. Extensive testing has shown that the preferred material for deformable body sections is polyurethane. Suitable grades have been developed for automotive use by leading material manufacturers and numerous examples of both material and external applications exist ranging from 'safety

Fig. 5.12   Porsche 928 flexible front and rear ends. (Courtesy Bayer AG)

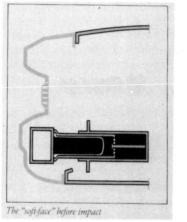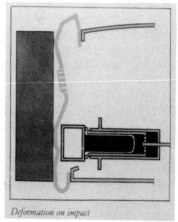

The "soft-face" before impact   Deformation on impact

*Fig. 5.13   Deformation and recovery of a 'soft' front end in Bayer's Bayflex
(Courtesy Bayer AG)*

cars', developed by Fiat and others, to the rear ends of New York
taxis.

Among some of the most sophisticated of applications is the
Porsche 928 (Figure 5.12) in which 'Bayflex', a polyurethane
integral skin foam system developed by Bayer, is used for both rear
and front ends. A characteristic feature of all 'Bayflex' grades is a
gradual transition between the continuous tear-resistant outer skin
and the cellular core. The skin and core are produced in a single
operation and are integral. The moulding for the 928 was developed

by Porsche in collaboration with Phoenix EG who also produce the sections. Deformation under impact and recovery is shown in Figure 5.13.

5.6 FASCIAS: MOULDABILITY REQUIREMENTS, WEIGHT SAVING AND INTEGRATION

One of the most beneficial applications of plastics in the interior of the car is the dashboard, or fascia. This major component, hitherto a composite and predominently metal assembly in plastics, can be produced in a single injection moulding operation. Material development has produced suitable resins for the application which, because of the size and complexity of the modern dashboard, demands good resin flow properties coupled with stiffness, good impact resistance, colour fastness and resistance to heat distortion. Various materials are in vogue. Examples include Dow's Pulse A30-105 PC/ABS thermoplastic resins are used for the centre console of the BMW Series 5 cars. (Figure 5.14). The use of another Dow resin, Tyril San XZ 95104.50, for injection moulded glove compartment doors on BMW 3 and 5 series cars, have solved the problems associated with breakage at some critical areas in the moulded part.

General Motors have reduced the cost of a number of dashboard parts in the Vauxhall Cavalier by the use of polypropylene instead

Fig. 5.14   Dow thermoplastic resins are used in the central console of some BMW cars. (Courtesy Dow)

of ABS. The components include glove box, deposit box, centre cover, fuse cover and the cover over the instrument panel. Mouldings are made by Injection Moulded Plastics of Hoddesdon in the United Kingdom who worked closely with Hoechst Celanese and Opel to overcome potential problems. Mouldflow was used to determine gating positions and a hot-plate welding system was developed for assembly of the glove box lid together with a cold forming method for producing the integral hinge of the fuse cover.

The dash panel and its supporting structure of the Nissan Bluebird is an example of a complex assembly which is built-up from several components. 'Procom' D1038, a mineral filled grade of polypropylene developed by Imperial Chemical Industries (ICI), is used for the main components. The material specification involved passenger impact tests since the panel was required to deflect sufficiently to prevent over-severe deceleration of the passenger's head while at the same time absorbing energy over a reasonable distance. All these factors were coupled with the requirement that surface shattering would not occur in a pattern which again might cause injury in the event of a frontal impact. In addition to 'Procom' mouldings for the instrument cluster, the panel assembly incorporates a 'Diakon' MG 102 acrylic lens which covers the instruments themselves. Behind the panel is the heater duct which is moulded in ICI 'Propathene' GZM 124, an unfilled polypropylene.

Other interior mouldings in the Bluebird include rear quarter panels, glove box interior, luggage compartment side trims and integral parcel shelfs. All are moulded in 'Procom' T 20 C557, a low distortion grade containing 20% talc filler. This grade supplied to Audi, General Motors and Ford among other European manufacturers, is characterised by a 'satin' textured finish. It is increasingly being used to replace ABS in many areas. Talc filled 'Procom' T 20 C556 is used by Carello Lighting to mould the Bluebird headlamp housings, the total weight of these mouldings is said to be some 32kg per car.

The dashboard of the Ferrari Mondial, 2.9 litre, V8, a single moulding of considerable complexity, is produced by RIM technology in ICI's polyurethane by Macchi Arturo S.p.a. in Italy (Figure 5.15). The assembly houses not only the instrument panel and minor controls but also the ventilation and demisting outlets and the radio loudspeaker housing. The component is an excellent example of the flexibility of the RIM design which incorporates fine detailing, deeply dished areas, a first class finish and a careful balance of strength and weight through variation in thickness throughout the different areas of the moulding. The right hand version of the Volkswagen Corrado also uses a polyurethane

*Fig. 5.15   The dashboard of the Ferrari Mondial is a single moulding produced by
RIM technology in ICI polyurethane. (Courtesy ICI)*

instrument panel moulded in RRIM by Marley Foam who operate
one of the largest RRIM polyurethane presses in Europe.

Advanced concepts in dashboard design include those of General
Electric Plastics Europe, specialists in the area. Designs
incorporate integrated air channels and vents in the main armature
moulding, with a line through the central console to provide rear
seat passengers with ventilation. The design which meets ECE
impact requirements, allows freedom for either right- or left-hand
drive variants plus model differentiation by the application of
'softfeel' finishes. The Noryl (PPO/PA GTX alloy) grades are
available in a complete range of colours which satisfy the industry's
colour fade requirements. Other areas of the car's interior in which
the integration theme is followed include headliner panels
incorporating sun visors, auxiliary instrument display modules,
courtesy lights and rear view mirror mouldings. Plasticised
Baymond L 2418, new ethylene vinyl acetate copolymer from
Bayer, a semi-rigid PVC sheeting, is used for instrument panel
fascias, door trim and central consoles. The thermoformable
sheeting has excellent long-term ageing properties, low fogging
values and good light stability.

The widespread use of liquid crystal displays on the instrument
panel has been advanced by the application of Makrofol LT, a glass

*Fig. 5.16   Bayer's Transflex film is used for the liquid crystal display on the Fiat Tipo
instrument panel. (Courtesy Bayer AG)*

reinforced polycarbonate introduced by Bayer AG. One example
of the use of the film is in the liquid display on the instrument panel
of the Fiat Tipo (Figure 5.16) produced by Borg Instruments of
Remchingen, Germany. The film provides excellent internal light
diffusion, good light transmission, high stiffness and flame
retardability. The film also offers good printability and die cutting
properties so vital for the production of high quality information
carriers and provides even illumination when lit from behind. It can
be printed to reflect incident light and provides the necessary heat
resistance to withstand the high temperature concentration that can
build-up when halogen lamps are used.

5.7   WINDOWS AND WINDSCREENS: SEALING, TEMPERATURE AND CORROSION RESISTANCE

The gasketing and sealing of windscreens and rear windows is an
area in which advances have been made to speed fitting and reduce
breakages. Examples include the external seal in Lapthene TPE, by
British Artid Plastics, which is used to seal the tailgate window in
the Rover 800 Fastback range. The material, a flexible
thermoplastic elastomer, remains flexible and dimensionally stable

Fig. 5.17   Bayflex MP polyurethane integral skin foam facilitates the gasketing of automobile windows. (Courtesy Bayer AG)

over a wide temperature range and is aesthetically acceptable. In addition to sealing the glass in the rear window, the extrusion covers a channel for the wiring loom which carries power to the wiper/ washer, window heater and tailgate light. Rapid fitting and reduced breakages are also advantages acrueing from the use of Bayer's Bayflex MP, an integral skin polyurethane foam system. Produced by RIM technology, flexible PU gasketing (Figure 5.17) compensates for minor distortions and, with all the necessary anchoring elements insert moulded, permits automated assembly by robot equipment. The gasketing imposes no restrictions on design, the inclusion of sharp corners, variations in wall thickness and the incorporation of mini-spoilers. Problems often associated with low temperature in laminated windscreens are reduced by the use of Adimoll DH, a new plasticiser based on di-n-hexyladipate, specially developed by Bayer AG for the production of polyvinyl butyral (PVB) film, used in safety glass screens.

Other advances in windscreen and rear window production is the use of plastics to replace metal hitherto used almost exclusively for wiper arms. If wipers are to function properly, particularly at the high speeds now attainable, the material must have a high degree of stiffness so that the pressure of the blade on the screen always remains constant. One material, Pocan, a 30% glass reinforced

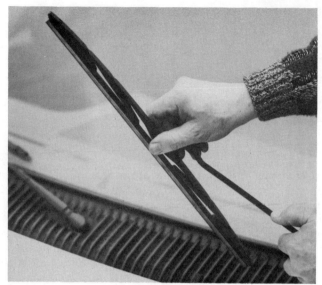

Fig. 5.18   Glass fibre reinforced Pocan PBT is used to replace metal for windscreen wiper arms. (Courtesy Bayer AG)

polybutylene terephthalate from Bayer satisfies this requirement, has minimal water absorption, good UV stability and resistance to cleaning fluids, antifreeze and de-icing salt. (Figure 5.18).

5.8   LIGHTS: GLASS REPLACEMENT AND REAR LIGHTS

The clarity and impact resistance of polycarbonate has been instrumental in its use as a replacement for glass. More recently improvements in the quality and the development of surface coatings to resist scratching and in UV resistance has permitted its use in more demanding applications such as headlights. In Europe the market for automobile headlamps is estimated at some thirteen million units/year. In Japan and the United States manufacturers including Ford have used polycarbonate for a number of years. In Europe uptake has been hampered largely due to the lack of an accepted standard. Now, however, there are development programmes being undertaken by leading headlamp manufacturers including Bosch, Carello and Cibie and Hellyer. European units have been used on models for export to the United States by Peugeot, Rover and Volvo. Polycarbonate producer Bayer has developed a range of grades specifically for application in

automotive headlamps. Grades are 'Makrolon' AL 2443, low
viscosity, UV stabilised; Makrolen AL 2447 with similar properties
and featuring easy mould release features and 'Makrolon' 2647,
medium viscosity, UV stabilised and also featuring easy mould
release characteristics. Advantages of these grades over glass are
light weight, higher fracture resistance due to excellent impact
strength, greater freedom of design and economical processing by
injection moulding methods. Other characteristics arc high heat
resistance, a light transmission of over 87% (at 4mm thickness) and
excellent colour stability at elevated temperatures. Technical
requirements of headlamp lenses demand surface treatment to
improve scratch resistance, delay UV degradation and improve
solvent resistance. A number of coatings are available, including
silicone treatment from General Electric Silicones/Sherwin
Williams, an acrylic treatment developed by Mitsubishi Rayon and
a propriety treatment developed by Morton International.

Various plastics including glass fibre reinforced materials are in
general use for injection moulded headlamp bodies and reflectors;
all require a number of processes to produce the final component. A
French automotive accessory manufacturer, Neiman Lighting &
Signalling Equipment of Sens, has developed a system for making
headlamp reflectors using Du Pont's Minlon engineering
thermoplastic and Zytel nylon resins which has led to lower costs
and a more sophisticated design (Figure 5.19). The sandwich
moulding-cum-direct metallising technology eliminates several

Fig. 5.19   French lighting specialist, Nieman Lighting and Signalling Equipment, use Du Pont Minlon and Zytel resins for moulded headlamp reflectors. (Courtesy Du Pont)

manufacturing steps hitherto needed with metal reflectors. The system permits the whole reflector, including highly stressed attachment tabs, level adjuster and flashing direction indicator to be produced in a single operation. The Du Pont material was chosen for the load-bearing structural element because of its dimensional and thermal stability characteristics. Its high heat distortion temperature of 237°C is combined with a sharp melting point and an isotropic shrinkage of only 0.5%. The latter property of the moulded part is of major importance, especially when, with dipped beams, spot temperatures may vary from 120°C at the base of the reflector to 190°C at the top.

Side lights: rear light clusters

Front and rear light clusters have long been familiar as plastics mouldings and over the years have become more sophisticated in design and complex in form as body shapes become advanced aerodynamically. Today most rear clusters incorporate in addition to the mandatory red tail, brake and reversing light indicators, a powerful, integrated light which is coupled to the reversing gear to show light behind the car. Choice of material in these areas has, in the main, been an acrylic which provides the required transparency, colour fastness and resistance to road salt and washing fluids. Cluster designs vary from the minimum requirements of rear, brake and reverse indication to massed groups extending over a large area of the rear body.

Production methods, as discussed in Chapter 2, also vary widely depending on the complexity of the assembly and in many cases on the model quality. Four-colour rear clusters also incorporating amber and clear lenses are common throughout European models and in a number of cases are produced by specialist moulders. Figure 5.20 illustrates a typical three-colour rear cluster in ICI Diakon acrylic. Four-colour rear clusters for the Murat (Fiat) Dogan and Sahin models are injection moulded in Diakon PMMA by Plastas Plastik Saneti ve Ficaret AS of Istambul for the Fiat licencee in Turkey. Another European automotive lighting specialist, producers of a wide range of original and replacement components, is Yorka among who's products are the rear light assemblies for the Cadillac Allante designed by Pininfarina and recognised as the most prestigious model of the General Motors range. The body of the car is assembled in Italy and then flown to the United States where the vehicle is completed in Detroit. Reportedly only some thirty six cars are produced each day and each carries a seven year or 100,000 mile warranty. Thus with

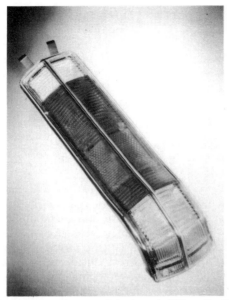

Fig. 5.20   Typical three-colour rear light cluster in ICI acrylic. (Courtesy ICI)

quality rather than quantity at a premium, the production methods
are singular. The rear light cluster is a multi-layered construction
incorporating an intermediate layer injection moulded in 'Diakon'
CMH 454L clear 011. The moulding is hot foil printed in a striped
pattern in white, maroon, gold, silver or black to complement the
colours of the bodywork. The external layer is moulded from a
combination of the same Diakon grade as the intermediate layer
and a red grade 4088 which provides both weather protection and
good optical qualities. The inner layer adjacent to the bulbs is
currently of polycarbonate because of its temperature resistance.

The light housing is also produced by Yorka in Spain and is of
grey ABS vacuum metallised by the company prior to assembly.
One of the most critical operations in the production of the cluster is
the hot-foiling of the intermediate 'Diakon' layer. Each part is
printed in three operations, middle, right and left-hand curved
sections. Other stages in assembly are ultrasonic welding together
of external and intermediate lenses and the application of the words
'Cadillac Allante' and metal strips to the exterior. As a final
operation all joints of the 1800mm long assembly are vacuum tested
to ensure a watertight seal.

A demarcation from the normal system of injection moulding the
housings of rear light clusters in a traditional thermoplastic is

demanded in the case of the Lotus Esprit by the extensive reshaping of the rear of the car to fulfil aerodynamic requirements at high speed. This is a good example of the way RRIM polyurethane can be used to reduce tooling costs and fulfil the details of the change. The deep dish shaped housing is moulded in self-colour and can be painted in body colour.

5.9 SEATING: REGULATIONS, WEIGHT SAVING, RECLINE MECHANISM, FOAM FABRIC

Prototype work by ICI in injection moulded seats for JCB excavators in 'Propathane' polypropylene indicated many advantages as compared with steel frames. These include, lower weight (up to 4kg/g vehicle), greater design flexibility including the possibility of coloured, textured or fabric decorated surfaces direct from the mould, fewer parts and improved comfort with better lumbar support by virtue of the shell-type squab. Prototype seats developed to meet ECE safety regulations were designed with either a solid seat pan or perimeter framed sprung unit (Figure 5.21). A solid pan together with PU foam cushioning enabled Propathane GW 213 to be used, while the perimeter frame design, with its higher point loadings, was moulded in HW 60 GR30, a 30% coupled glass fibre reinforcement. Seat recline mechanism was in Maranyl nylon 66 which permitted a complete recline mechanism to be designed giving a weight saving of nearly 2kg/vehicle. Other features of the design included a conveniently forward located hand wheel for recline control and optional drive either manual with high bevel gearing or motorised adjustment using a low geared worm drive.

An early concept in high volume automated seat design, patented by the Ford Motor Company, Gammar AG, in Germany, incorporated vacuum foam filled pad and cover assemblies which clip into lightweight fully-stressed steel frames in the case of the backrests and partially-stressed injection moulded, sprung shells for the cushion. The covering fabric is vacuum formed prior to polyurethane foam being injected in a two-shot process.

Development work directed to foam-in-fabric seating by companies such as Bayer, BASF and ICI has led to its use by Ford Europe, Chrysler in the United States and Renault in France. Research and development work by ICI has resulted in the development of suitable MDT-based, cold cure flexible polyurethane foam systems for foam-in-fabric applications using both barrier and non-barrier techniques. Non-barrier techniques

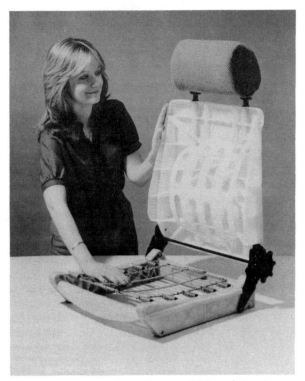

*Fig. 5.21   Prototype sprung seat designed to meet ECE regulations incorporates ICI
Propathane and Maranyl (nylon), recline mechanism. (Courtesy ICI)*

were used by several French moulders for the Renault Super 5. The
introduction of unit seating by Chrysler was the first use of MDI
based cold cure polyurethane foam in the United States (Figure
5.22).

The Volvo Car Corporation of Sweden has approved Dow
Europe's new cold-cure-moulded 'Specflex' polyurethane sealing
system which totally eliminates the need for environmentally
disruptive Chlorofluorocarbon (CFC) blowing agents in the
foaming process. Volvo was the first end user to approve the system
following its use on a trial basis by Sylvan of Sweden who use PU
foam to mould seats for Volvo. The system is based on Methylene
diphenyl diisocyanate (MDI) instead of toluene diisocyanate (TPI)
which is used in other PU seating systems. In the all MDI Specflex
system, water replaces CFC as the blowing agent. The water reacts
with the MDI to form carbon dioxide, producing a foam which
creates the cell structure. The resulting foam density is $50kg/m^3$.

Fig. 5.22   Chrysler front seat features the use of cold-cure polyethylene foam.

Fiesta front seats (Figure 5.23), produced by unit technology, are used both in Dagenham in the United Kingdom and Valencia in Spain for the upgraded model. They also incorporate plastic seat shells developed jointly by Ford and Bayer AG. The shells are injection moulded in Bayer's Novodur P2K, a non-reinforced ABS with high impact strength and heat resistance. The seats feature integrally moulded anchoring points for the seat cushion and sprung wire mesh Pullmaflex mat. The seat shell supports the seat cushion assembly which is produced by a one-step direct injection foam-in fabric process to give a seat cushion complete with insert moulded anchoring and fixing elements.

An all-plastics car seat prototype developed by Bayer AG and introduced at Kunststoffe '89 in Dusseldorf, demonstrated the feasibility of a front seat with a load bearing structure of thermoplastics (Figure 5.24). The materials used were Durethan BKV 130, an impact modified, glass reinforced nylon 6 which was chosen for the load bearing structural elements of the seat and back and, for cosmetic reasons, the non-structural side trim. 'Novodur'

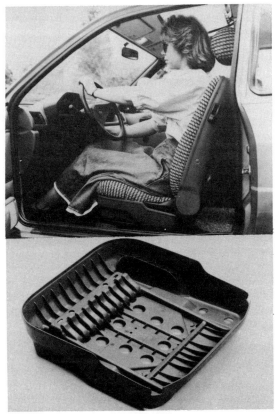

Fig. 5.23   Front seats for the Ford Fiesta are moulded in Bayer's Novodur P2K non-reinforced ABS and incorporate Pullmaflex mat. (Courtesy Bayer AG)

P24, a high impact, low temperature resistant ABS was used for the shell that supports the seat cushion and Bayblend T 05 MN, a thermoplastic blend of 'Makrolon' polycarbonate and 'Novodur' for the energy absorbing unit. 'Batfit', a cold moulded polyurethane foam produced by the multiple mixing head (MMK) method gave differential hardness zones for the centre and sides of the seat cushion. The covering fabric was Bayer's polyacrylic 'Dralon' fibre. This velvet fabric has a pleasant handle, good durability, is light fast and easy to clean. The seat back reclining mechanism and head restraints of the prototype were modified standard components produced by the Kliper-Recaro company.

In discussing developments in automotive seating technology mention should be made of the work carried out by BASF

Fig. 5.24 Prototype 'all-plastic' seat incorporates nylon, ABS, moulded polyurethane foam and polyacrylic fibre. (Courtesy Bayer AG)

Elastogran, in Germany, on foam-in-cover production using a RIM dispensing machine. The system is used along with others in the Ford Fiesta in Europe and the Chrysler Minivan in the United States. The design has been passed to Hennecke (Mobay Machinery Group) and Krauss-Maffei for production.

5.10   CARPETS AND HEADLINERS

Car carpeting, often taken for granted in the past, is an important marketing area in the automotive field. In Europe and the United States major automobile manufacturers have tended to use the more traditional fibres such as nylon and rayon whereas the Australian car industry have for many years used Shell polypropylene for carpeting. Traditionally automotive carpeting was of the cut-and-sew type which, although popular, was expensive. The later development of moulded carpets simplified fitting and were of excellent appearance. As would be expected, the specification for trim in Australia is particularly stringent with regard to fastness to light, as vehicles there are subjected to long exposure to strong sunlight, often intensified by large areas of glass. Polypropylene in the form of spunbonded 'Typar' and 'Elvax',

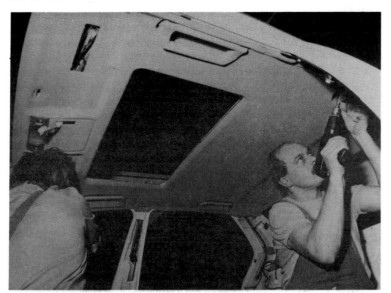

Fig. 5.25   Headliners for the BMW Series 7 models, made of glass mat reinforced polyurethane integral skin foam are both light and strong. (Courtesy Bayer AG)

ethylene vinyl acetate resin by Du Pont now find wide application as a lightweight carpeting material. 'Lycra Spandex' fibre is also used in upholstry and trim fabrics.

Recent developments in headlining materials include the introduction by John Cotton of Calne, United Kingdom, of a sandwich construction lining for the sunroofed version of the Vauxhall Cavalier. The sandwich construction incorporates two layers of woven glass fibre mat, a polyurethane core and features a foam-backed, washable PVC decorative cloth which can be wiped down to remove the inevitable shading experienced in vehicles used in urban conditions. Also recently developed for use in the MMW 7 Series is a headliner made from Bayer's polyurethane integral skin foam, Baydur GMV, glass mat reinforced. Although only 2-3mm thick and lightweight, the liners are easy to fit and extremely strong (Figure 5.25).

Whilst discussing plastics in the car's interior mention should be made of their application in the 1990 Corvette ZR-1 (Figure 5.26). Sheller-Globe, the automotive interior systems manufacturer that co-developed, designed and engineered the interior components of the ZR-1 with Chevrolet in the United States, selected 'Cadon' 127 and 'Lustran' 446 ABS from Monsanto Chemical Company of St Louis for many of the components. 'Cadon' is used in the car's glove

Fig. 5.26   Applications of Monsanto materials in the 1990 Corvette ZR-1 include glove box and central console mouldings

box and inner door. It combines superior heat resistance with excellent processibility and low cost. In this application high-heat performance is important because the exterior aerodynamic styling and steeply raked screen of the ZR-1 can result in high interior temperatures. 'Lustran' 446 ABS is used for the floor console, an application in which it offers cost benefits, good processibility and lightness, while providing the necessary strength to support the car's electrical components.

6
Recycling

6.1 CAR POPULATION INCREASE: DUMPING, ROUTES TO MATERIAL RECOVERY AND SORTING

The increasing use of plastics in the passenger car inevitably raises the question of its disposal when the car's useful life is at an end. Research by IKV, Aachen, German indicated that the average life of a car built between 1975 and 1995 will be some ten years and that at the present rate of usage the proportion of plastics materials will have risen from some 5% in 1975 to 13% or more by 1995. However this could well be an underestimate – the increasing application of engineering plastics and composites suggests the latter figure could well approach 20% of the total weight of the vehicle.

The number of vehicles registered since 1980 and ready for scrapping was of the order of 2.6 million in 1990. The corresponding figure for 1984 was 1.2 million and in 1996 will be some 2.8 million. These findings highlighted by Anton Weber of BASF give some indication of the extent of the problem in the coming years.

Currently the majority of companies specialising in the disposal of scrapped cars use equipment designed for the recovery of metals. Their practice is to dump the plastics and other material content which together account for about 25% by weight of the total. In the UK and in Germany in particular legally controlled dumping sites are becoming fewer, more expensive and increasingly the practice is subject to criticism by the environmental lobby. In addition to the political implications, there are pressures from the steel industry to limit the use of plastics in cars because of its effect on the sales of steel. Points raised by established car scrappers range from requests that not less than 70% of the weight of the vehicle should be steel, PVC should not be used because of its low combustion heat, to demands that fuel tanks should always be of steel to facilitate emptying prior to shredding.

With the increased use of plastics, car shredders will have less recovered metal to sell and at a price which has already dropped significantly. In Germany steel scrap prices have taken a downturn since the early 1970s from some 200DM/tonne to less than

100DM/tonne due to over capacity in the scrap industry. However, with todays developments in processing plastics scrap the way is open for the recovery industry to benefit from the inevitable increase in the usage of plastics in the automotive industry. Of the three routes to the treatment of plastics scrap, chemicals can be recovered in a number of ways. Pyrolysis reduces scrap to combustible gas, carbon black and aromatic oils for petrochemical use. Evidence of interest in this process is highlighted by the sponsoring of research at Hamburg University by the German Federation of Plastics Manufacturers which has led to the setting up of a 10,000 tonne/year plant at Eberhausen.

Pyrolysis has been used to recover poleofins from scrapped cars but the process is currently uneconomic because of the relatively low price of petroleum. It is anticipated that if the price of crude oil should rise by a factor of, say, three the process could be developed to provide a successful means of material recovery. Polyurethanes, polyesters and polyamides can be treated by hydrolysis. They are dissociated at high temperatures in the presence of water. Polyols can be liberated from pure polyurethane scrap such as, for example, material obtained in the production of automobile seating which can in turn be reconverted into polyurethane foam. While in theory the recovery and recycling of plastics scrap is the most attractive option from an environmental point of view and in certain cases one that can also be economic, the problems associated with its reuse are separation of the different polymers and the hand labour entailed. Large single polymer components and assemblies such as dashboards, consoles and bumpers offer better opportunities for economic recycling. A move recommended by the Association of German Car Manufacturers to identify the material on all major plastics components would be an additional incentive to dismantle selectively a scrap vehicle.

In an effort to advance the process of economic recovery of plastics materials, the West German Association for Research in Automotive Engineering have commissioned Porsche to investigate a scheme for designing a vehicle that would lend itself to easy dismantling. The aim of the project was to separate the parts and assemblies into individual types of plastics that could be recycled without the problems associated with sorting. A medium sized vehicle on the market was analysed to obtain general guidelines for a design which would favour economic dismantling. The vehicle chosen contained some 97kg of various types of plastics of which some 63% could be sorted; 46% of the total (73% of the fraction that could be sorted) was accounted for by parts consisting of a given type of polymer. The total time for dismantling all the

Table 6.1 THERMOPLASTICS MATERIALS USED TO
PRODUCE ASSEMBLIES THAT COULD BE DISMANTLED
FROM A MEDIUM SIZE STANDARD PRODUCTION CAR IN
20 MINUTES. (COURTESY BASF)

Material	Weight (kg)
Polypropylene	15.4
Polyethylene	8.7
ABS/ASA	5.4
Polyoxmethylene	0.4
Polyamide	0.07

Table 6.2 A SUGGESTED SEQUENCE FOR DISMANTLING THE PARTS AND
ASSEMBLIES (COURTESY BASF)

Assembly	Cumulative time (s)	Weight (kg)
Front bumper	90	5.98
Rocker panel	120	6.692
Rear bumper	270	12.370
Map pocket on door	330	14.272
Side swipe strip	410	16.156
Fuel tank	830	24.675
Rear shield	860	25.244
Door window-seal	900	25.965
Tool box	910	26.128
Roof lining	920	26.298
Air filter	1010	17.725
Screen-wiper linkage cover	1020	27.860
Radiator expansion tank	1060	28.375
Front wheel-arch shell	1180	29.844
Radiator cover	1195	30.017

parts and assemblies was approximately 74 minutes with a further
41 minutes for parts dismantling and sorting into individual classes.
A breakdown of the thermoplastics parts and assemblies
dismantled in 20 minutes is given in Table 6.1. Table 6.2 shows a
suggested sequence of dismantling.

6.2 OVERALL BUMPER SYSTEMS

In many cars today bumpers are an integral part of an overall system
comprising bumper support, energy absorbing foam, trim and
fixing devices. In some models lamps, grille and spoiler are also
integrated. In cases where the various components are moulded in
different materials individual polymers are obviously difficult to
separate and grade and for this reason it is only the large area parts
such as bumper covers that in many cases are dismantled prior to

shredding and subsequent recycling. However if the entire bumper system consists exclusively of a single polymer such as polypropylene, recovery is facilitated and usually economic. Such a system, developed by BASF, incorporates a flexible supporting base of polypropylene. The energy absorbent core is of Neopolen polypropylene foam having resilience and a volume weight of between 30 and 80g/litre depending on specific requirements. Both the foam and support are enclosed in an elastic, low temperature, impact-resistant Novolem polypropylene copolymer. The system is completed by a tough, good adhesive strength coating by the BASF Lacke und Farben AG range of materials. Lamp casings, grilles and spoilers can also be moulded from unreinforced or reinforced polypropylene. In this way the entire integrated bumper system can be shredded as a whole, requiring no sorting, and can be homogenised in a compounding extruder to produce a pure grade product consistently with favourable properties.

6.3   INTERIOR ASSEMBLIES

Another area highlighted by BASF refers to large assemblies such as instrument panels, door side trims and rear window shelves which can be moulded in pure grade polypropylene. Normally, an instrument panel comprises three individual parts – the supporting base, usually of reinforced thermoplastics or pressed wood fibres, glass mat-reinforced polypropylene (Elastopreg), or an injection moulding of reinforced polypropylene. An interlayer of semi-rigid polyurethane foam is located above the base and the entire construction is covered by a thermoformed, flexible film usually consisting of a blend of polyvinyl chloride (PVC) and an acrylonitrile/butadiene/styrene copolymer (ABS). In principle, polyurethane can be replaced by polypropylene foam. In this case a prefoamed core is used. The more elegant solution however is to fill the space between the base and sealing film with pre-expanded polypropylene pellets. Promising experiments have been conducted aimed at replacing the thermoformed PVC/ABS film with flexible polypropylene. However the development of polypropylene dashboards will take some time due primarily to the problems associated with installing the polypropylene foam.

   Door panels in polypropylene can be developed more easily and the technique is already at an advanced stage. The individual components of the trims such as the base, decorating film or textile can be exclusively of polypropylene as can the armrest and door pocket. These examples demonstrate the technical feasibility of recycling large, pure grade components that can be easily dismantled.

6.4   RECYCLING PLASTICS FUEL TANKS

Blow moulded fuel tanks as compared with their steel equivalent, discussed in Chapter 3, have many advantages. They allow greater freedom in design, thus optimising the space available for their location, are lighter and have increased capacity, size-for-size, which coupled with trouble free production methods has been instrumental in their greater use. In North America moulded tanks fitted in 1988 numbered some one million, with projections that this figure could double by 1991 and double again for the mid 1990s. Weighing on average 7kg, the moulded tank represents another major plastics assembly of interest to the recycling industry.

The problems associated with the recycling of fuel tanks has been the subject of an investigation, among others, by BASF in the framework of the Working Group on Material Recycling organised by the Association of Plastics Producing Industries (VKE). Initial results from a study involving 100 used fuel tanks, have from a technological point of view, encouraged more extensive measures to be initiated in order to use recycled material as the basis of high quality components. In the investigation, after removal of all parts not made of high density polyethylene, tanks were steam cleaned and cut into two to facilitate aeration. The halves were ground to increase surface area and dried for five days at 100°C in an atmosphere of nitrogen to extract as much as possible of the remaining gasoline. In the case of diesel tanks it was found that an insufficient quantity of fuel was removed and, as with the gasoline tanks, the expenditure of energy and labour was too great to make reclaim by this method economically viable. For this reason degasification in a twin screw extruder was studied for seven different screw variants. Results showed that extremely short treatment periods were necessary and that rapid drying under vacuum was preferable in order to obtain high quality ground material.

Today, the automobile and plastics industries work in close cooperation and as applications for established and newly developed polymers and composites continue to expand considerable attention is being given to solving the remaining problems of disposal or preferably recycling by a number of Europe's leading companies. In Germany four major chemical manufacturers have investigated the possibilities of recycling for four widely used automobile plastics. In addition to the work carried out by BASF in the recovery of high molecular weight polyethylene from fuel tanks, Hoechst have investigated the recovery of impact modified polypropylene from bumpers, Bayer the recovery of glass reinforced nylon and ABS from wheel hub caps and Huls the recovery of polypropylene from used battery cases. The ease with which each material could be recovered and its quality when recycled varied. The recovery of polypropylene from battery cases presented the least problem, ABS wheel hub caps required considerable outlay on paint removal. However tests on the wheel cap material showed that 90-95% of the strength obtained with virgin material was retained but some doubt was expressed that the material recovered from these and the other components could be resold at an economic figure.

6.5 COMPOSITES

The recycling of plastics composites raises other problems because of the difficulties of separating the constituent polymers. Regranulated composites, as with mixed polymers, can often be used as core materials in multi-component injection of parts such as bonnet hatchback and engine shielding panels. The recycling of advanced composites incorporating expensive reinforcement can be economic. The matrix can be removed by the use of solvents or by thermal oxidation to make the reinforcement available.

As discussed by Norbet Jung of BASF, in drawing up an energy balance sheet for composites, both the energy consumed during the production of a component as well as the operation of the finished product has to be taken into account. A study conducted by Audi has demonstrated that the energy consumed during production accounts for only 10% of the total energy of a car. Due to their light weight potential, composites offer clear advantages – the energy required in the production process has an extremely short pay-off period.

The recycling of used composites renders the energy balance even more favourable – not just that of advanced composites but also that of components composed of glass mat-reinforced thermoplastics (GMT), sheet moulding compound (SMC), and bulk moulding compound (BMC), which are reinforced by relatively short, mostly non-oriented glass fibres. However, the recycled compounds must not result in a weight increase over and above new parts. This would in turn create an increase in fuel consumption and exhaust emissions.

A multi-stage recycling process for these composites is being developed. In the first stage used SMC parts undergo a shredding procedure that is designed to ensure that the glass fibres are shortened as little as possible. The process produces oblong particles a proportion of which can be added to the material used to produce the new parts. Material composition and some of the mechanical properties are changed as a result. An increase in the proportion of recycled material results in a decrease in flexural strength, tensile elongation and impact strength, it does not impair rigidity. Currently the optimum proportion of recycled material in SMC parts in terms of costs, mechanical properties and surface quality is put at about 25%.

The second recycling stage planned is a 100% particle recycling process with resin admixture. At this stage mouldings requiring lower stress resistance such as floor panels can be produced. After this stage the material has been so extensively exploited that incineration is the only possibility. However, experiments conducted by the AKV (Arbeitsgemeinschaff Verstarkte Kunststoffe – Working Group on Reinforced Plastics) have demonstrated that the gases given off are environmentally compatible. Additionally, the energy recovered amounts to 10MJ/kg of composite material, so that the energy balance discussed becomes even more favourable.

6.6 THERMOPLASTIC COMPOSITES

Glass mat-reinforced thermoplastics containing mainly polypropylene have been available for only some ten years and thus still represent a comparatively small section of the market. As discussed earlier, they exhibit high resistance to dynamic stress and are particularly suitable for structural components such as car seats and multi-functional supports. A major factor in their economic recycling is the availability of pure grades which offers the possibility of first remelting the used parts and then directly remoulding them into new components without the intermediate stage of manufacturing semi-finished products. Studies carried out by BASF have shown that two reprocessing stages are feasible without major detriment to properties. Up to the third reprocessing stage, relative solution viscosity – a direct indicator of the chain length of the polymer and hence the state of the material – undergoes only minor changes although it changes markedly at subsequent stages. Loss in mechanical properties, on the other hand, is relatively small, amounting to approximately 20%. These findings indicate that during the first recycling stage, the material recovered is well suited to the production of relatively uncritical parts such as engine compartment shields, battery mounts and foamed plastics inserts.

The second recycling stage produces material of a quality suitable for such items as industrial pallets and similar products which are subject to lower dynamic stress. In a demonstration, parts made by Elastrogran cotained some 20kg of used GMT parts.

The processing of glass mat-reinforced plastics into short glass fibre-pellets for injection moulding of items including items such as those containing a central core is another alternative. During granulation, post-stabilisation and chemical recoupling of the product are possible. There is a marked enhancement of properties ranging between those of talcum-reinforced and glass fibre-reinforced polypropylene.

6.7   CURRENT ACTIVITY

In Europe companies active in the recycling of packaging are investigating the opportunities offered by an extension of operations to include new business in the dismantling and recovery of polymers from other products notably in the automotive industry. As mentioned, DSM (Dutch State Mines), have commenced the processing of bumpers from Volkswagen and Audi cars to produce material which Volkswagen will mould into new bumpers. Volkswagen has a car dismantling plant at Leer in Germany where used bumpers are reduced to small pieces which are subsequently washed and regranulated by Reko at Beek in Holland. Upgrading and recompounding of the reclaimed material to Volkswagen's specification is carried out by DSM Speciality Compounds at Genk in Belgium. The Volkswagen bumpers are moulded from DSM materials including 'Stamylan' polypropylene 'Kellan' elastomer modified and 'Kelburon' reactor modified propylenes. Du Pont is setting-up a recycling facility at Limburg in the Netherlands for the processing of polymer based material from its plants in Europe. The plant is central to Du Pont facilities in Germany, Belgium, Luxembourg and the Netherlands and will apply the recycling and upgrading technology that the company has used in the USA.

Another major European materials manufacturer, General Electric Plastics has set-up a major recycling initiative in conjunction with Ravago, the Belgian compounding specialist. They will investigate methods for upgrading material which can be used as part of the 'Cascade' concept aimed at the reuse of materials over a number of cycles. Other links are with AMA Cars of Munich where engineering plastics scrap will be separated and regranulated for reuse and with Kotrac in the Netherlands who in conjunction with General Electric Plastics have developed technology for the recovery and regrinding of automotive mouldings on a mobile basis.

General Electric Plastics also supply materials for the BMW Z1 convertible, a vehicle which is heralded as the first model to have all its vertical panels injection moulded in thermoplastics. As described in Chapter 5, the Z1 contains some 60kg of General Electric materials. The front wings, doors, rear quarter panels and rocker panels are moulded I Xenoy polycarbonate/PBT alloy, the front and rear fascias are in Lomod thermoplastic elastomer and the side door supports and rocker panel reinforcements are of Azmet glass mat reinforced thermoplastics from General Electric's subsidiary Azdel.

In the United States, automotive recycling has hitherto been identified with mountains of rusting vehicles. It has now been transformed into a high-volume, metal reclamation industry and one in which the increasing use of plastics promises to transform the business further. Automotive recycling companies use a metal shredding process to cut cars into strips of metal, plastics and cloth for subsequent separation into rotary magnetic drums. The process winnows the lighter shredded plastics and cloth materials from the metallic remainder. The result is the separation of ferrous scrap, non ferrous scrap and what is termed 'fluff', which includes plastics, rubber, cloth and glass.

Luria Brothers, a Cleveland based division of Connell Ltd, note that the problems associated with 'fluff' produced by the winnowing process will undoubtedly increase as the use of plastics materials in vehicle bodies rises. However, as the average age of standard production cars shredded in the US is ten to twelve years, they do not expect to handle large quantities of body panels for some while. The majority of materials will be from items such as bumpers, rocker panels and fascias. In a few years, the new generation of US plastics bodied cars such as, for example, the Fiero will be coming to the end of their service life. It is questionable however that classics such as the Corvette range and imported and cherished European marques with plastics bodywork will ever fall into the hands of the reclaimers.

7

Special construction – prototypes

The pressures to make cars more economical and aerodynamically better, with improved corrosion resistance and general durability has called for changes in design, materials and production methods. As discussed elsewhere, the automobile industry is, understandably, reluctant to dismantle complete production systems which have been refined through the years and replace them with a new system at considerable cost. The economic and quality improvements that have resulted from developments in press tools and robot spot welding techniques now permit the production of a car in a considerably shorter time than hitherto. To initiate change and introduce new materials a number of companies and organisations have set up research facilities to bring together the expertise of the plastics and automotive industries.

7.1   EARLY PROJECTS

Among early projects was the ECV-3 (Energy Conservation Vehicle) project by B.L. Technology, British Leyland's research arm, which was aimed at producing a car with fuel consumption figures better than any other petrol-engined concept car had claimed to date. The ECV-3 (Figure 7.1) is the result of a four year research and development programme in which all areas of vehicle design, engineering and manufacturing technology have been investigated to produce an experimental family vehicle of advanced specification, performance and economy. The ECV-3 was not intended to be a production car but was hand-built to show the advances possible in automotive technology which could influence car manufacture from the mid 1980s into the 1990s. Objectives included the following quantitive targets: maximum speed: over 100mph, acceleration 0-60mph; under 12 seconds, fuel consumption: urban, 50mpg, 56mph, 80mpg, 75mph, 60mpg. These fuel consumption figures are 60-75% better than most typical

Fig. 7.1   The ECV-3 Energy Conservation Vehicle by B.L. Technology

cars of comparable size and performance, and could only be achieved – even with improved engine performance – by reducing both weight and drag to some two-thirds of the current norm.

The first requirement was met by using an aluminium monocoque structure. The majority of the body panels were of glass-reinforced reaction injection moulded polyurethane (RRIM). The material used was Bayer's Bayflex GR. The front end was moulded at the company's plant in Leverkusen. The bonnet and inner components of the tailgate were prototyped to simulate Sheet Moulding Compound (SMC). RRIM polyurethane was chosen in preference to high strength steel or aluminium alloy for a combination of reasons, ie low weight, cost and suitability for quantity production processes, including painting, corrosion resistance and damage resistance.

The entire unpainted body structure including doors and tailgate, but without glass, weighed 138kg, a saving of some 125kg compared with a modern steel structure of comparable size and stiffness. While this is the largest single saving, there is a knock-on effect throughout the rest of the car. For the same performance a smaller engine, transmission, brakes, wheels and tyres can be used. The aerodynamic body shape, flush glass, rear spoiler and 'clean' underbody with engine, gearbox, exhaust and other components out of the airflow, produced a drag coefficient of 0.25, a figure well under the best achieved by any production car and equal to the best known experimental vehicle. The inside space was comparable with the Sierra, Cavalier and other similar models. The reduced weight coupled with a specially designed 1.1 litre, 3-cylinder all-alloy engine permitted the ECV-3 to better all the targets set with a speed in excess of 115mph, an acceleration of 0-60 in under 11s and a typical fuel consumption of 63mpg.

Search for improved fuel/performance ratios, coupled with faster production methods also encouraged the use of low-profile SMC for external panel work. Peugeot chose SMC for the majority of the panels of its VERA research vehicle (Figure 7.2). Based on the Peugeot Model 305, the project embodies all the proposed plastics materials that were feasible for production. The front wings were moulded in ABS to evaluate weight savings and to establish the possible reduction in the number of parts in the steel assembly. ABS also had the advantage of being thermoformable and could be painted without the need for special treatment. By reducing body weight by some 99kg, it was possible to reduce the size of the engine, gearbox, suspension and the wheel diameter to obtain an additional weight saving of about 70kg. The VERA prototype was thus some 20% lighter, 28% more aerodynamically efficient and 63% more economical than the production 305 vehicle. It has highlighted the future possibilities of plastics materials for external bodywork but has also highlighted the problem of painting in-line should the project be translated into commercial production.

Fig. 7.2   The VERA research vehicle by Peugeot is based on a Model 305

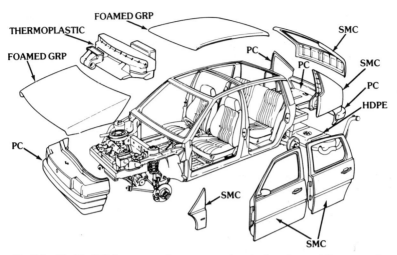

Fig. 7.3   The Fiat V.S.S. prototype incorporates nine plastics subassemblies mounted on a load-bearing steel frame. (Courtesy Plastics Design Forum)

Fiat in Italy also researched energy efficient vehicles, using methods similar to those applied in the USA, where the concept of cladding a structural frame removes the panels from any stress-bearing function. The Fiat VSS (Vettura Sperimentale a Sottosistemi) experimental subsystem vehicle based on the company's Ritmo, employed a load-bearing steel frame to obtain rigidity and passenger safety and thus allowed the designers to use plastics to their full advantage. With external dimensions identical to the Ritmo, the VSS body was 20% lighter than a conventional car, quieter and, while meeting international safety regulations, exhibited a fuel saving of some 6 to 7%. The vehicle (Figure 7.3), was designed with ten subsystems, nine of which were of plastics that could be produced separately and supplied to the assembly line as complete units. The system could thus reduce the production time by some five hours as compared with that of the Ritmo currently running at the Rivalta plant in Turin. The front unit incorporating the radiator grille, air intake, front bumper, headlamps and the rear unit and rear bumper were all of polycarbonate. The front bumper and assembly was mounted on a steel frame so that in the event of a minor collision the mouldings would deform without distorting the frame.

Polycarbonate was also used for the boot sides and floor rear cross-member and bumper. Front and rear wings, hatchback and both front and rear doors were of SMC, stiffened with a steel cross-bracing which also carried the hinges, locks and window winding mechanisms. The bonnet which reduced the four-part conventional steel component to a single moulding and extended to the wheel arches was in glass-reinforced foam polyester. It incorporated an air duct and weighed some 13kg as compared with the 17kg of the metal component. Foamed polyester was also used for the roof as an insulator and is bonded on assembly to the metal frame. The project exhibited weight savings of 32% and 18% on the front and rear doors respectively, 30% on the bonnet and engine compartment and 20% on the rear hatch.

In Germany, the universities of Aachen, Berlin, Darmstadt and Stuttgart in cooperation with Volkswagen, Daimler, Benz, Audi and Bayer AG carried out a programme of research designated Auto 2000. The project highlighted the use of polyurethanes. In the Daimler Benz prototype the bonnet, bumpers and window surrounds were of microcellular polyurethane reinforced with 20% of milled glass produced by the RRIM process and painted with a special coating system based on Bayer's Desmodur and Desmophen materials.

In the Volkswagen 2000, requirements demanded that the front end be designed so that it could be preassembled, be self-supporting, light, simple to fit and fulfil all safety requirements. The moulding, produced by RIM technology, incorporated bumpers and headlamp apertures and was mounted on a low profile SMC cross-member by a simple clamp. The cross-member itself, designed to withstand impacts of up to 2.5mph, was strengthened locally by varying the wall thickness and the glass content of the moulding. The rear end incorporates a similar combination of materials. An SMC member extended up to the boot lid whilst the lower portion supported the rear polyurethane shell. All components were painted with special coatings developed by Bayer. Of particular interest, in the context of plastics usage were the flush-fitting quarter lights and rear side windows which were of polycarbonate with a scratch-resistant silane-based coating. The system, designed to last the lifetime of the car, fulfilled all optical and de-icing tests and was some 35% lighter than glass.

The most innovative of the Auto 2000 projects from the four universities was the 'Uni-Car' which incorporated a number of features from the Pedestrian Safety Vehicle, a modified Opel Ascona built by technicians at Bayer and Berlin University. Additional to increased pedestrian safety and reduced drag were the aims of improved economy, efficiency and environmental acceptability. The front end incorporated an outer layer of Bayer's Bayflex semi-rigid foam with an energy absorbing cushion of semi-flexible foam to form the rear bumper. To reduce the possibility of injury to pedestrians, the low front bumper and swept back panel eliminates the effect of the leading edge of the bonnet. The headlamps were also recessed for safety. In a conventional vehicle, the front end is comprised of some twenty individual components. However, by the use of RIM it was possible to reduce the assembly to two pieces. To reduce head injuries to pedestrians, the surface of the bonnet was also made of foam and was of aerodynamic form. The underside incorporated a layer of flexible polyurethane foam which, unaffected by engine temperature, reduces engine noise. Polyurethane foam was also used for the windscreen surround, for the aerodynamically designed side windows and as door frame padding. In a similar manner to the other projects, all external plastics and metal surfaces were painted with the specially formulated coatings described.

7.2   CURRENT PROJECTS

The Vector 1 shown by General Electric Plastics at the 1987 Sitev show in Geneva underwent a full road testing programme necessary to be passed by all roadworthy passenger vehicles before the K'89 Fair in Dusseldorf where Phase 2 of the Vector programme was shown. The Vector 1 is based on a Citroen AX frame and includes bumpers, tailgate, rear panels and under-bonnet components produced in General Electric Plastics materials. With Vector 1 as a running development, Vector 2 which is expected to be seen on the road in 1995, incorporates a thermoplastic bonnet and a new interior concept including a composite instrument panel and thermoplastic doors of two-material GTX/TPS construction. The tailgate is also of two-material construction consisting of a Noryl/GTX nylon modified PPO outer moulding bonded to a glass mat reinforced thermoplastic GMT stampable sheet component, based on Azdel polypropylene, with a steel frame for additional stiffness.

7.3.   BLOW-MOULDED BODY PANELS

General Electric Plastics is widening its processing technology into the blow moulding of certain components, as opposed to injection moulding. One example is the debut of Alpha 1, a machine built in Germany by Krauss-Maffei for installation in the company's US research centre. The unit is capable of consecutive operations involving several different methods of processing including injection moulding, flow forming, stamping, structural foam moulding, combination moulding and gas-melt moulding. One attractive possibility is the capability of stamping a composite sheet to shape, prior to injection moulding a high quality surface. For body panel development the system would produce a composite with a grade 'A' surface.

7.4   DU PONT APV PROJECT

Earlier chapters have discussed the APV vehicle designed by Du Pont, built by Automotive Design in the UK and show at K'89 in Dusseldorf. The project, which highlights the application of plastics in all areas of the car, is intended to demonstrate that the company is in step with its automotive customers and stresses the need to reduce production costs, improve quality and achieve a faster response to design requirements. The project which incorporates some 30% by weight of plastics illustrates how total weight savings and aerodynamic efficiency can be accomplished leading to lower fuel and running costs through the selective use of polymers. The project features reinforced body panels and doors as well as polymers in trim, drive chain and electronic systems.

Fig. 7.4   Demonstration model at K'89 shows the application of plastics materials.

7.5 CARMAT 2000 PROJECT

Current research projects also include the Carmat 2000 part of the EEC's programme to produce a production-ready design which takes advantage of both new materials and advances in production technology. The resultant vehicle is intended to be capable of competing, from a users point of view, with one built by conventional means, be attractively styled, as safe as possible, have a similar performance and provide better economy. With the widespread use of plastics materials it will no doubt be comfortable and certainly quieter. However, the over-riding factor remains, it must be cheaper to produce than its conventional counterpart. An additional factor is that the major body panels should be capable of being recycled.

The project is being led by PSA, the French manufacturer of Peugeot and Citroen, with a major contribution from ICI. The company's Advanced Materials Group supply many of the panels, doors, wings and the boot lid. ICI has many years of experience working with the automotive industry and some time ago set-up a Motor Industry Group (MIG) to coordinate and identify potential advances. The current project, commenced in 1987, will last for five years with the results intended to be unveiled by PSA in 1992. The lessons resulting from the project will not be known until later but it can be anticipated that while the technology used in the automotive industry will not undergo an immediate transformation, the knowledge resulting from the application of new materials and production methods will show manufacturers the way to produce better, quieter and more corrosion resistant vehicles without actually leading, as yet, to the 'all-plastics' car.

Apart from the application of new materials, notably long fibre-reinforced thermoplastics, the project embraces the use of numerous advanced production techniques, such as the sandwich moulding (Section 2.4) of major panels and the production of hollow components by the gas melt technique pioneered by Battenfeld, Cinpress and others (Section 2.5). These techniques permit the designer to achieve a combination of light weight with stiffness and a reduction in 'sink' marks.

7.6 RACING CAR RESEARCH

Designers of racing cars, notably in Formula 1, have to fulfil a number of criteria. The designer has to house and protect the driver, accommodate sufficient fuel for a full 200 mile race, support

Fig. 7.5   The Moneytron Onyx ORE-1 Grand Prix car shown at the Materials for Design Exhibition illustrates the aerodynamic form of Formulae 1 racing cars. (Courtesy 3M, United Kingdom PLC)

a powerful rear engine and gearbox, both of which must be readily accessible, support front and rear suspensions and lastly, but importantly in view of the very high speeds attained, provide an overall aerodynamic shape. One of the major problems facing designers has always been to ensure maximum stiffness and strength in the structure to permit tuning of the suspension according to the characteristics of each different circuit. Research has shown that the structure is subjected to a lateral load of up to 4g under braking, down force, vertical and side impacts. Currently the use of carbon fibre-reinforced composites which can increase specific modulus and specific strength by some 25% on a straight replacement basis over metals, offer a solution in the case of a 'no costs barred' Formula machine. Additionally the mouldability of these reinforced plastics composites in a monocoque situation permit strength and stiffness of the structure to be coupled with maximum aerodynamic efficiency.

While the development of Formula 1 machinery does not strictly fall into the category of prototype vehicles as discussed, the performance of new materials and design technologies can be examined on a much shorter lead time in the highly competitive sport of motor racing than compared with other equally demanding areas of endeavour.

Apart from advances in monocoque structures, the 1990 season has seen the development of a number of joint projects. Among these has been the use of a thermoplastic/carbon fibre composite from ICI designated APC-2 PEEK from which gearbox selectors have been machined. The new units, which can withstand oil temperatures of up to 150°C, weigh some 63% less than the 270g counterpart so saving over 1kg when used in the multi-ratio gearbox at the rear of the vehicle. Other developments have been in the areas of composite wheels, drive shafts and underpanels. Lighter composite wheels, while having the advantage over die cast aluminium units of reducing unsprung weight, have to withstand tyre temperatures of up to 100°C and, in areas adjacent to disc brakes, temperatures which can be as high as 700°C. Drive shafts which are required to handle very large impulse and running loads again pose physical problems. Under-panels or diffusers, also critical components which are required to withstand not only exhaust gases and high temperatures in the vicinity and the rear engine but also abrasion on the track are a challenge to the consortium.

8

Reinforcement

8.1   EARLY SYSTEMS

In previous chapters reference is made to reinforcement of both thermosets and thermoplastics. Fibrous and granular materials are used, the latter such as talc, wood flour, glass microspheres and similar inert materials largely in injection moulding to extend the polymer, increase rigidity and as the core layer in sandwich mouldings. These materials act as fillers rather than true reinforcement. One of the earliest uses of glass fibre as a reinforcing medium in polyester resins (GRP) was in automobile bodywork. The combination of the two materials permitted the body designer greater freedom to produce difficult contours and complex double curvatures without recourse to the use of costly, time consuming and highly skilled operations of wheeling and panel beating when producing specialised body designs in metal.

Original moulding methods were based on hand layup of glass fibre mats using open moulds. As technology advanced these primative methods gave way through spray-up systems to the more sophisticated closed-mould methods (Section 2.16) and the use of pre-located long fibre reinforcement. The development of an injection moulding process whereby chopped glass fibre reinforcement could be incorporated in a polyester resin (Section 2.7) without damage to the fibre opened the way to the more rapid and economic production of large automotive body panels.

The good mechanical strength properties of glass mat laminates, in conjunction with pre-impregnated polyester materials (SMC), has now been used to advantage in combination with thermoplastics, notably polypropylene. The prepared material permits more rapid moulding cycles to be achieved than are possible with thermoset laminates. In contrast to all other glass fibre reinforced plastics, glass mat reinforced polypropylene laminates are made with endless fibre mats and provide particularly good reinforcing effect. The special structure of mats made with E-glass facilitates good flow of both mat and melt so that the fibres become evenly distributed right to the edge of the moulding.

8.2 GLASS FIBRE TYPES: ROVINGS, SIZING, DENSITY

Glass fibre reinforcement is available in a number of forms and with different types of size which, applied as a liquid during production, protect and bind the fibres during processing and perform specific tasks during the incorporation of the reinforcement in the resin. Filaments destined for spray-up rovings are coated with a hard size whilst those used for weaving of cloth and tape will have a softer size applied. In all cases the size will contain a keying agent which is compatible with the resin and designed to promote adhesion between the two, i.e. a film former and lubricant system. The coupling agent is usually an organic silicone compound and the film former a polyer in emulsion such as polyvinyl acetate. The lubricant is usually based on acid amines. In most cases other constituents are included to provide specific properties such as anti-static characteristics.

Roving, in which many strands are gathered together with a mechanical twist, is used in spray-up processes and to produce chopped strand mat used in hand layup moulding and in the more sophisticated closed-mould method. In chopped strand mat the random bundles of filaments are treated with a binder, usually a polyvinyl emulsion or a polyester powder, both of which are soluble in the laminating resin and are selected to be of a suitable strength to hold the fibres in place during processing.

In the material produced by Owens Corning Fiberglas, the 75 tex strands are bonded together with a highly soluble polyester compatible silane (RO7E) size. This product is designed for use in the manufacture of sheet moulding compounds, ie is easily chopped, is distributed with minimum static, has good wetting properties, easy flow during moulding and good surface quality, all vital characteristics. Type RO7EX1 is available with a bare glass linear density of 2400 or 4800g/kgm.

8.3 GLASS FIBRE MAT: CHOPPED STRAND, NEEDLED AND VEIL MAT

Types of mat include needled varieties which are similar to chopped-strand mat but with the exception that the fibres are held together by a mechanical needling process rather than by a chemical binder. Types are also available for use with specific moulding methods, for example, press moulding. They have the advantage of good drape characteristics and wet-out rapidly giving good strength retention. Surfacing or veil mats are ultra light and are used next to gel coats to provide a smooth surface finish and to block-out fibre pattern. Continuous strand mats are used largely in resin injection systems to obviate fibre 'washing' and strand displacement. Woven rovings are heavy, drapable material available in the form of cloth in which weft and weave bundles of fibre are at 90°. Woven cloth and tape vary in weight, thickness and weave. They are materials which today do not find wide application in automotive work.

8.4   SHEET MOULDING COMPOUND (SMC)

This material is available in a number of varieties of polyester resin paste/glass combinations formulated to suit specific requirements. Originally they were categorised as one of three basic types or grades; general purpose, low shrink and low profile. A distinction between these three types is in the formulation of the resin systems. General purpose SMC has only unsaturated polyester resin as the base ingredient; low shrink SMC may contain up to 30% thermoplastic polymer by weight of the basic resin while low profile SMC systems contain some 40% of thermoplastic. The development of sheet moulding compounds made a notable impact on automobile bodywork production, one example being the early use of the material in the Chevrolet Corvette body which used outer panels of SMC produced in matched metal moulds.

The strength characteristics of SMC mouldings are influenced not only by the type of resin and filler used but to a greater extent by the amount and type of glass fibre reinforcement incorporated. Basically, there four types of glass reinforcement. Chopped rovings of some 25 to 50mm in length are distributed randomly to provide equal strength in all directions. This type gives a good surface finish and has a glass content of some 25 to 35%. A second type incorporates endless rovings which are arranged parallel and longitudinally to chopped fibres to increase strength in one direction. In a third type, rovings 100 to 300mm in length are laid parallel but staggered, a form that is said to provide optimum flow characteristics during moulding. Lastly, a wound formulation of crossed roving tapes laid at 20° provides very high directional strength.

8.5   GLASS FIBRE REINFORCED THERMOPLASTICS

The need to replace metal parts with reinforced plastics has led to techniques for reinforcing thermoplastics with fillers and in particular with glass fibres. It is not possible to make a clear cut division between reinforcing materials and fillers. Specific applications demand variation in the type and quantity of the materials incorporated. In general, properties required are rigidity, lack of heat distortion, hardness, compressive strength and tensile strength. Early development involved glass reinforced nylon but more recently there have been advances in equipping other thermoplastics, notably polypropylene, and including PA, ABS, SAN, PE, PC and PETP with reinforcing and filler materials. The main reinforcing or filler materials are glass, asbestos, calcium carbonate, silicates, mica and wood flour. Each imparts special physical properties which affect the processing as well as their subsequent application. The content of reinforcement in the compound can be up to 50% by weight and with fillers up to 70 to 80% by weight.

Long glass-fibre reinforced thermoplastics feature high impact strength, stiffness and dimensional stability. Long glass-fibre reinforcement is often compared with short glass fibres which, as already mentioned, offer corrosion resistance, cost/weight advantages and ease of processing. For injection moulding (Section 2.7) short glass fibres, usually some 5mm in length, are melt mixed in a polymer and extruded into pellets. This is a high shear process which results in significant fibre breakage and random fibre dispersion within the pellets. Long glass-fiber pellets can be produced by proprietary pultrusion methods whereby continuous, undirectional fibres are individually impregnated with resin and formed as a rod or tape that is subsequently pelletised. In this process which creates less fibre damage, long fibres extend the full length of the pellet at a length of 10 to 15mm. Long glass-fibre thermoplastics are replacing diecast aluminium, magnesium, zinc and brass with performance improvements up to five times greater in strength-to-weight ratios. At high fibre loadings, long glass-fibre thermoplastics compete in tensile strength and permit more complex shapes to be moulded than with metal. Additionally, these components can substantially reduce fabrication costs by eliminating assembly time and secondary finishing operations.

Continuous glass-fibre mat reinforced polypropylene sheet produced by Smalit of Switzerland has been developed for rapid processing by hot flow stamping on metal stamping and standard compression presses. Mouldings made from glass mat reinforced thermoplastics are very uniformly reinforced and combine the advantages of unsaturated polyester resins, e.g. high strength and rigidity which is maintained in all directions, coupled with the processing advantages and design latitude of thermoplastics.

Glass mat reinforced thermoplastics are processed in a similar manner to SMC's by flow moulding using high speed moulding presses. The cut-to-size blanks are heated to a forming temperature of 200°C and moulded in cooled moulds using very short cycles of 20 to 50 seconds, whereas cold polyester SMC blanks are moulded in a heated mould on very much longer moulding cycles. Moulding or 'stamping' at high forming temperatures allows components of varying cross-section with fully reinforced bosses and ribs to be produced. The polypropylene laminate is manufactured continuously. Several layers of glass mat impregnated with a special polypropylene melt are combined to form an endless, completely impregnated sheet material of maximum width 1000mm, maximum length 2400mm, thickness 3.7mm and weight approximately 4.5kg/m^2. The standard content is 40% by weight of glass fibre.

In contrast to other glass reinforced plastics, glass mat reinforced polypropylene laminates incorporate endless glass fibres, achieving good strength characteristics. The special structure of mats made with 'E' glass facilitates a good flow of mat and melt so that fibres are evenly distributed right to the edge of the moulding. The sheet and cut-to-size blanks can be stored indefinitely and at present are available in black and natural colour. If required, other materials such as decorative laminates, films and textiles coverings can be laminated on top of the sheets during manufacture and in some cases can be applied during the moulding process. Typical properties of stamped Symalit GM40 polypropylene components are shown in Table 8.1

Table 8.1   TYPICAL PROPERTIES OF STAMPED SYMALIT GM 40 POLYPROPYLENE COMPONENTS. (SOURCE, SYMALIT CO LTD)

Property	Units	Din	Value
Specific gravity	g/cm^3	53479	1.19
Glass content	%/by weight		40
Flexural strength	N/mm^2	53452	152
Flexural modulus	N/mm^2	52457	5515
Tensile strength	N/mm^2	53455	75
Tensile modulus	N/mm^2	53457	5200
Elongation at yield	%	53455	3−5
Heat distortion temperature	°C	53461	156
Coefficient of thermal expansion	K^{-1}	52328	27×10^{-6}
Dielectric strength	k/Vcm	53481	121

8.6   BULK MOULDING COMPOUND (BMC)

Bulk moulding compound, sometimes referred to as dough moulding compound, is used to a certain extent for the production of relatively small, compact components. The material is produced by mixing a suitable catalysed polyester or epoxide resin, a mineral filler, pigment and chopped glass fibre reinforcement to form a dough-like material which can be used in matched metal moulds or can be injection moulded using a specially designed plunger type machine. Some breakdown of the glass fibre occurs during preparation which results in some reduction in strength as compared with components containing long glass fibres. However, loss of strength is acceptable for many ancilliary automotive components which are not subject to high stress.

8.7   CARBON FIBRE

High Modulus Carbon Fibre (HMCF), known as Graphite Fibre in the USA, has been accepted as a viable commercial reinforcement for plastics, taking its place with glass, aramid, ceramic and boron fibres. HMCF was developed initially at the Royal Aircraft Establishment, Farnborough, England and by Rolls-Royce as a reinforcing material for use with thermosetting and thermoplastics resins to provide a higher modulus than glass fibre at a lower density than aluminium for use in the aircraft industry. It is now finding increasing application in the automotive industry for highly stressed applications, notably monocoque construction racing car bodywork.

Almost all HMCF is produced by converting a polyacrylonitrile (PAN) precursor fibre using various carbonisation techniques. The many grades of HMCF can be classified into four main varieties: Ultra-High Modulus (UHM), High Modulus (HS), Very High Strength (VHS) and High Strength with the range of properties shown in Table 8.2. Two major forms have been developed from

Table 8.2   COMPARISON OF CARBON FIBRE REINFORCED PLASTICS WITH GLASS REINFORCED PLASTICS AND OTHER STRUCTURAL MATERIALS. (SOURCE, WORLD WIDE CARBON FIBRE DIRECTORY)

Material	Specific gravity	Youngs modulus (Gpa)	Specific modulus (Gpa)	Ultimate tensile strength (Gpa)	Specific strength (Gpa)
CFRP *	1.55	130	83.9	1.6	1.03
GRP *	2.0	41	20.5	1.3	0.65
Aluminium	2.8	72	25.7	0.46	0.165
Steel	7.8	207	26.5	1.0	0.12
Titanium	4.5	110	24.4	0.93	0.207

* 60% volume, unidirectional reinforcement in epoxy resin

Table 8.3 BUMPERS AND FASCIAS

Model	Part	Weight (kg)	Process			Polymer		Reinforcement	
			RIM	Com	Gmt	PU	UP	MF	SMC
Ford Cosworth	Front bumper	4.48	•			•		•	
Lotus Excel	Front bumper	4.00	•			•		•	
Renault 21 Turbo Sport	Front bumper	5.30	•			•		•	
Renault Espace	Front bumper	4.50		•			•		•
Alfa Romeo 75 (USA)	Front bumper beam	4.00		•			•		•
Audi 90	Front bumper beam	2.94		•			•		•
BMW 300 Series (E30)	Front bumper beam	4.80		•			•		•
BMW M3	Front bumper beam	5.60		•			•		•
Mercedes 190	Front bumper beam	3.00		•			•		•
Mercedes 'S' Class (USA)	Front bumper beam	8.60		•			•		•
Peugeot 505 (USA)	Front bumper beam	7.20		•			•		•
Renault 21 Break + US	Front bumper beam	6.00		•			•		•
BMW M3	Front bumper cover	–	•			•		•	
Alfa Romeo 164	Front bumper fascia	4.600	•			•		•	
Lancia Thema	Front bumper fascia	4.500	•			•			
Peugeot 205	Front bumper fascia	3.300		•			•		•
Porsche 924	Front bumper fascia	5.80		•			•		•
Reliant Scimitar SS1	Front bumper fascia	4.85		•					•
Renault Alpine V6-GT	Front bumper fascia	5.60				•		•	
Renault Super 5	Front bumper fascia	5.50				•		•	
Renault Alpine V6-GT	Front end fascia	2.75	•			•		•	
Porsche 944 Turbo	Front spoiler	4.50	•			•		•	
Renault 21 Turbo Sport	Front spoiler	2.00	•			•		•	
Renault 21 Turbo Sport	Side protective panel	1.30	•			•		•	
Lotus Esprit (Fed) Turbo	Rear bumper	4.50	•			•		•	
Renault Espace	Rear bumper	3.00		•			•		
Alfa Romeo 75 (USA)	Rear bumper beam	4.00		•			•		•
Audi 90	Rear bumper beam	2.55		•			•		•

Audi 5000 (US)	Rear bumper beam	5.10
BMW 500 Series	Rear bumper beam	5.30
BMW M3	Rear bumper beam	6.30
Mercedes 190	Rear bumper beam	2.90
Mercedes 'S' Class (Europe)	Rear bumper beam	3.60
Peugeot 505 (US)	Rear bumper beam	7.40
Renault Alpine V6-GT	Rear bumper beam	3.35
BMW M3	Rear bumper cover	9.50
Alfa Romeo 164	Rear bumper fascia	5.20
Alfa Romeo 75	Rear bumper fascia	5.20
Lancia Thema	Rear bumper fascia	5.10
Lotus Excel	Rear bumper fascia	4.00
Peugeot 205	Rear bumper fascia	2.90
Porsche 924	Rear bumper fascia	5.30
Reliant Scimitar SS1	Rear bumper fascia	3.30
Renault 25	Rear bumper fascia	6.90
Renault Alpine V6-GT	Rear bumper fascia	5.30
Renault Super 5	Rear bumper fascia	4.50
Renault Super 5 GT Turbo	Rear bumper fascia	7.60

Legend: Tables 8.3 to 8.11

Processes

Com = Compression moulding
RTM = Resin transfer moulding
HLU = Hand layup (wet)
RIM = Resin injection moulding
GMT = Stampable thermoplastics
IM/BMC = Injection bulk moulding compound
Inj = injection moulding

Thermosets

PU = Polyurethane
UP = Unsaturated polyester

Thermoplastics

ABS = Acrylonitrile-Butadiene-Styrene
PA = Polyamide
PBT = Polybutylterephthalate
PC = Polycarbonate
PE = Polyethylene
PPO = Modified polyphenylene oxide
POM = Polyacetal
PSU = Polysulfone
SAN = Styrene-Acrylonitrile
PP = Polypropylene

Glass reinforcement

BMC-CS = Bulk moulding compound
CS = Chopped strands
Mat-CS = Chopped strand mat
Mat-Cont = Continuous strand mat
SMC = Sheet moulding compound
MF = Milled fibres
WR = Woven roving

Table 8.4 BODY PANELS AND PARTS

Model	Part	Weight (kg)	Process			Polymer					Reinforcement		
			RIM	Com	Gmt	PU	UP	MF	SMC	Mat-CS	Mat-C	CS	BMC-CS
Rolls Royce	Airdam	4.00	•			•		•					
Fiat X1/9	Body-bumper trim	0.80	•			•		•					
Reliant Rialto	Bonnet (hand layup)	3.50									•		
Reliant Scimitar SS1	Boot (hand layup)	10.00					•			•			
Renault 25	Bottom line (injection)	0.23					•					PP-CS	
Alfa Sud Sprint	'B' pillar cover	0.30		•					•				
Citroen BX	'C' pillar cover	1.00		•					•			PA-CS	
Audi 80 Coupe Quattro	'C' pillar grille (Inj)	0.10							•				
Citroen BX, BX Break	'C' pillar grille	0.70					•		•				
Mercedes 190 (Injection)	'C' pillar grille	0.25					•					PC-CS	
Porsche 928	'C' pillar grille	0.25		•					•				
Saab 900 (Injection)	'C' pillar grille	0.20										PA-CS	
Volvo 300 Series (Injection)	'C' pillar grille											PA-CS	
Audi Quattro	Deck lid	6.20		•			•		•				
Ford Escort	Door frame trim	2.00		•			•		•				
Opel Manta GTE	Door sill cover	1.45		•					•				
Renault Alpine V6-GT	Exterior door panel	2.94		•					•	•			
Renault Alpine V6-GT	Exterior rear body panel	5.61		•					•	•			
Citroen Visa	Floor side trim	1.50		•					•				
Volvo 480	Front end	3.00							•				
Porsche 928	Front part	3.50	•			•							
Renault Super 5 GT Turbo	Front wheel arch extension	0.57		•			•		•				
Renault Super 5 GT	Hatchback (inj/BMC/ roving)	0.00		•					•				•
Fiat Tipo	Hatchback (injection)	10.50											•
Renault Espace	Hatchback	13.00					•			•			
Renault Espace	Hood	6.10			•		•		•				
Volvo 480	Hood (2 pieces)	12.80			•		•				•		

Model	Part	Weight (kg)	Process WM	HLU	Various	Com	Inj	Polymer UP	PU	Reinforcement Mat-CS	Mat-C	SMC
Alfa Romeo 75	Lateral protection panels	4.00				●	●					
Renault Super 5	Lateral protection panels	5.00				●	●	●				
Renault Express	Rear door inner panels	3.00				●	●	●				
Porsche 928	Rear part	3.50				●	●			●		
Ford Escort Cabriolet	Rear quarter panels	1.00				●	●					
Citroen CX	Rear wheel cover	1.00		●		●	●					
Renault Alpine V6-GT	Roof	8.43		●	●	●	●					
Volvo 480	Roof trim	0.40						●				
Saab 16 Valve Turbo	Saab 'Aerokit'	10.82				●	●					
Mercedes S-Class	Side panels	8.00				●	●					
Ford Fiesta XR2	Tailgate spoiler	1.17							●			
Renault Alpine V6-GT	Underbody and structural parts	39.46		●			●	●				
Ford Fiesta XR2	Wheelarch extension (F&R)	1.08		●			●	●				
Land Rover	Rear wheel arches	0.64		●			●					
Citroen BX, BX Break	Roof trim rails	0.50		●			●					
BL Maestro MG	Rear spat	1.90		●			●					

Table 8.5 COMPLETE/PARTIAL BODIES

Model	Part	Weight (kg)	Process WM	HLU	Various	Com	Inj	Polymer UP	PU	Reinforcement Mat-CS	Mat-C	SMC
Reliant Rialto	Body	72.00	●									
TVR	Body	150.00		●				●		●		
Lotus Esprit	Complete body	160.00			●			●			●	
Lotus Excel	Complete body	155.00			●			●			●	
Reliant Fox	Complete body	95.00	●					●				
BMW 3	Deck lid	9.50				●		●				
Renault Alpine V6-GT	Floor	9.73						●			●	●
Reliant Scimitar	Underbody	32.00		●					●			

Table 8.6 SPOILERS

Model	Part	Weight (kg)	Iml/BMC	Inj	Com	RIM	PBT	UP	PU	PA	BMI-CS	Mat-C	SMC	MF	CS
Porsche 911 Turbo SC	Deck lid spoiler	5.20			•			•				•		•	
Audi 200	Front spoiler	1.90				•			•				•		•
BL Maestro HLE	Front spoiler	1.25				•			•				•		•
BL Metro Turbo MG	Front spoiler	3.00				•			•						•
BMW Alpina	Front spoiler	2.30			•			•				•		•	
Mercedes S-Class	Front spoiler	4.80				•			•				•		
Peugeot 505 (US)	Front spoiler	2.00			•			•				•		•	
Porsche 944	Front spoiler	2.70				•			•				•		•
Ford Fiesta XR2	Front valance	7.60				•			•				•		•
Ford Escort Cabriolet	Rear quarter panels	1.00												•	
Lancia Delta	Rear roof spoiler	1.30		•			•								
BMW 550. 600	Rear spoiler	1.50			•			•				•			
Mercedes S-Class	Rear spoiler	4.70				•		•					•		
Peugeot 305 GT	Rear spoiler	2.50	•			•				•					
Peugeot 309	Rear spoiler	3.50	•			•			•						
Peugeot 309	Rear spoiler	2.50				•			•		•				
Porsche 930	Rear spoiler	5.10			•			•				•			
Ford Cosworth	Rear spoiler insert	1.40			•					•					
BL Maestro MG Metro	Tailgate spoiler	0.55				•			•					•	
Volvo 480	Tailgate spoiler	0.40		•											
Lancia Thema, Thema SW	Trunk trim	0.25				•		•							•

Table 8.7 HEADLAMPS SURROUNDS, PANELS AND GRILLES

Model	Part	Weight (kg)	Process				Polymer						Reinforcement		
			Inj	Com	RIM	IM-BMC	PBT	PA	UP	PU	PP	SMC	CS	MF	BMC-CS
Mercedes 280 to 450S, SL, SLC, 190	Grille	1.10	•					•					•		
Ford Sierra Ghia	Grille, front panel	–						•					•		
Mercedes S-Class, Coupe, Sedan, SL, SLC, T-Class	Grille lower radiator	1.00	•				•						•		
Peugeot 505	Ext headlamp housing	0.35	•					•					•		
Volvo 480	Headlamp cover	0.30		•											
Opel Kadett, Monza, Rekord, Senator, Commodore	Headlamp housing	1.00	•							•			SAN-CS		
Saab	Headlamp housing	–		•							•		•		
Volvo 480	Headlamp housing frame	0.30	•	•								•	•		
Volvo 480	Headlamp panel	0.25		•					•			•			
BL Maestro	Headlamp reflector	0.45				•			•						•
Citroen AX	Headlamp reflector	0.43				•			•						•
Fiat Tipo	Headlamp reflector	0.55				•			•						•
Ford Sierra, Orion	Headlamp reflector	0.40				•			•						•
Ford Sierra, Orion	Headlamp reflector	0.40					•			•					
Lancia Thema	Headlamp reflector	0.50					•			•			•		
Rolls Royce Silver Spur	Headlamp reflector	0.50				•			•						•
Rover, all models	Headlamp reflector	0.50				•			•						•
Vauxhall Cavalier	Headlamp reflector	0.25				•			•						•
Volkswagen Jetta	Headlamp reflector	0.50				•	•		•						•
Mercedes 190	Headlamp surround	0.10	•							•			•		•
Rolls Royce Silver Spur	Headlamp surround	0.55		•						•		•			
Lotus Excel	Rear light cluster	2.00			•					•		•		•	

Table 8.8 TAIL LAMP HOUSING

Model	Part	Weight (kg)	Process		ABS	Polymer		PP	Reinforcement	
			Inj	Com		PC	UP		SMC	CS
Audi 89.90	Tail lamp housing	0.19	•		•					•
BMW 300 Series	Tail lamp housing	0.28	•							•
Mercedes 'S' Class	Tail lamp housing	0.25	•		•					•
Renault Espace	Tail lamp housings	0.40		•			•		•	
Volkswagen Caddy	Tail lamp housing	0.70		•			•		•	
Volkswagen Jetta	Tail lamp housing	0.25	•					•		•

124

Table 8.9 EXTERIOR PARTS

Model	Part	Weight (kg)	Inj	RIM	Com	PPO	PU	UP	PA	PBT	ABS	SMC	CS	MF	Mat-CS
			Process			Polymer							Reinforcement		
BMW 700	Air outlet grille	0.15	•			•							•		
Alfa Romeo Spider	Bumper fascia & endcaps	6.00		•			•							•	
BMW M3	Cover, entrance platform	5.60		•			•								
Citroen BX	Cowl vent	0.60	•						•				•		
Volvo 300 Series	Cowl vent	0.35	•						•				•		
Renault 25	Cowl vent top grille	1.00	•						•				•		
Citroen BX	Exterior mirror housing	0.23	•						•				•		
Ferrari Testarossa	Exterior mirror housing	0.35	•						•				•		
Ford Sierra, Escort, Orion	Exterior mirror housing	0.25	•						•				•		
Peugeot 205, 309, 505	Exterior mirror housing	0.20	•							•			•		
Peugeot 305	Exterior mirror housing	0.15	•						•				•		
Renault 21	Exterior mirror housing	0.60	•							•			•		
Volvo 480	Exterior mirror panel	0.10	•						•				•		
Ford Scorpio	Fuel tank flap	0.12	•						•				•		
Peugeot 405	Fuel tank flap	0.09	•						•				•		
Renault Super 5	Package tray	0.15		•			•						•		
Alfa Sprint	Rear wheel hub	0.10	•						•						•
Ford Fiesta XR2	Wheel arch flare	3.00		•			•						•		
Alfa Romeo 33	Wheel cover	0.25	•						•				•		
Fiat Panda, Regata, Uno	Wheel cover	0.50	•						•				•		
Jaguar	Wheel cover	0.50	•						•				•		
Opel Ascona, Rekord, Berlina	Wheel cover	1.20	•						•				•		
Peugeot 309 GTi	Wheel cover hub	0.08	•						•				•		
Seat Ibiza	Windscreen wiper support	0.10	•						•				•		
Fiat Regata	Rear spoiler insert	0.20	•								•				

Table 8.10 ENGINE BAY COMPONENTS

Model	Part	Weight (kg)	Process			Polymer						Reinforcement		
			Inj	RIM	Com	PPO	PA	UP	PBT	PP	SMC	Mat-CCS	MF	GMT
Porsche 911	Air cleaner duct	0.50	•				•						•	
Audi, all models	Air filter assembly	0.70	•				•						•	
Renault Espace	Air guide	2.00			•						•		•	•
Mercedes 200-280	Air inlet tube	0.20	•		•		•	•					•	
Saab 9000 Turbo	Air intake cooler tanks	–	•										•	
BMW 700 Series	Air outlet grille	0.15	•			•							•	
Volvo 200 & 700 Series	Camshaft belt cover	0.35	•						•				•	
BMW 300 series	Fan, radiator	0.30	•				•						•	
Renault Express	Water tank	0.33	•				•						•	
Citroen BX	Fan shroud	0.35	•				•		•				•	
Fiat X1/9	Fan shroud support	0.4	•										•	•
Citroen CX	Fan support	2.00												•
Peugeot 305	Air conditioner	0.22	•		•		•			•	•		•	
Peugeot 405	Air control duct (right)	0.12	•								•		•	
Ford Granada	Heater fan	0.15	•				•			•	•		•	
Fiat Uno	Radiator expansion tank	0.30	•				•						•	
Alfa Romeo 33, 75	Radiator top, base tanks	0.35	•				•						•	
Citroen BX	Radiator top, base tanks	0.50	•			•							•	
Mercedes, all models	Radiator top, base tanks	1.20	•				•						•	
Renault 4	Radiator top, base tanks	0.50	•				•						•	
Volkswagen, all models	Radiator top, base tanks	1.20	•				•		•				•	
Renault 9, 11	Radiator cooling tank	0.17	•				•						•	
Jaguar XJS	Expansion cooling tank	0.65	•										•	
Volkswagen Scirocco	Eng. noise damping cap	4.00											•	•
Renault 21	Fuel pump superior body	0.04	•		•		•	•					•	
Volvo 760	Grille support	0.02	•										•	
Porsche 911	Oil cooler housing	1.55	•											
Volvo 200, 700	Oil trap	0.15	•		•	•	•	•			•		•	•
Lancia Thema SW	Shock absorber cap	0.20		•								•		
Mercedes 190, 200, 300	Transmission noise cover	2.40	•				•	•			•		•	•

Table 8.11 INTERIOR, INSTRUMENT PANEL AND SEATING COMPONENTS

Model	Part	Weight (kg)	Process			Polymer						Reinforcement			
			Inj	RIM	GMT	ABS	PBT	PA	UP	PU	PP	CS	MF	SMC	Mat-C
Citroen BX	Front bucket seat insert	0.80	•												
Lancia Delta, Prisma	Interior door handle	1.10		•							•	•	•		
BMW 500 Series	Central console	0.60		•											
Alfa Romeo 75	Dashboard frame	1.05	•									•			
Innocenti	Ash tray	0.11	•												
Ferrari Modial	Instrument panel	6.00	•					•							
Ford Scorpio	Instrument panel retainer	1.20	•			•						•			
Lancia Delta	Instrument panel retainer	3.00	•			•						•			
Peugeot 505	Instrument panel support	0.30	•									•			
Mercedes 200, 300	Front arm rest	0.32			•							•			•
Lotus Series 3	Rear corner valance	1.50										•			
Mercedes 'S' Class, 190	Rear seat arm rest	0.26		•	•	•				•	•	•	•		•
Daimler Benz W124	Rear seat backrest	8.69									•	•			•
Renault Express	Seat guide end	0.40	•									•			
Audi Avant	Split rear seat back	5.80			•				•			•			
Lancia Thema SW	Hatchback interior trim	0.90	•							•		•			
Renault 4	Window frame	0.05	•						•		•	•			
Volvo 480	Gear shift housing	0.31	•						•		•	•			
Peugeot 405	Gear shift support	0.23	•	•					•	•	•	•			
Autobianchi Y10	Interior door panel	0.60	•								•				
Citroen 2 CV	Interior door panel	0.30	•								•	•			
Lancia Thema SW	Miscellaneous trim	1.15		•					•	•	•	•	•		•
Peugeot 305	Ventilator duct	0.22	•									•			
Alfa Romeo 33	Interior mirror housing	0.05	•					•				•			
Renault Express	Door opening device	0.04									•	•			
Peugeot 405	Pedal support	0.75			•									•	

the two produced by the carbonisation processes; undirectional pre-impregnated tape and woven fabrics which themselves are often impregnated.

Some examples of the numerous and varied applications of reinforced plastics materials in major areas of European passenger cars are shown in Tables 8.3-8.11. The tables list a selection of 1988 models, production processes, parts, polymers and types of glass fibre reinforcement used. In the main, transmission components and electrical parts are injection moulded in polyamide (PA), with chopped strand glass fibre reinforcement. It should be noted that inevitably changes in materials and component design will have occurred that will to some extent affect the accuracy of this information. The data has been supplied by courtesy of Owens Corning Fiberglass Ltd.

Bibliography

Advanced Materials, No. 1, ICI Advanced Materials, PO Box 6, Shire Park, Bessemer Road, Welwyn Garden City, AL7 1HD, UK (1989)
Automotive Design, Himont USA Inc, Wilmington, Delaware, USA (1984)
Automotive Engineering, BASF Plastics, AG, D-6700 Ludwigshafen, Germany
Automotive Performance Plastics, Engineering Plastics Division, Hoechst Celanese, 26 Main Street, Chatham 07928, NJ, USA
'Automotive Report', *European Plastics News*, p. 81–94, October (1989) UK
Wood, R., *Car Bodywork in Glass-Reinforced Plastics*, Pentech Press Ltd (1980)
Carbon Fibre, Hyfil Ltd., Avonmouth Road, Avonmouth, Bristol, BS11 9DU, UK
Lovell, D.R., *Carbon and High Performance Fibres Directory 4*, Pammac Directories, High Wycombe, UK
Ceramic Fibres for the Automotive Industry, BP Chemicals, Belgrave House, 76 Buckingham Palace Road, London, SW1W 0SU, UK (1990)
Closed-Cell Polyethylene Foams, BXL Plastics Ltd., Virginia House, 56 Warwick Road, Solihull, W. Midlands, B92 7HU, UK (1990)
'Designing with High-Performance Plastics' in Off-the-Road & Automotive Equipment Applications, Rogers Corporation, Rogers, Conn 06263, USA
Design a Success with Delrin, Zytel Minlon, Rynite, Du Pont (UK) Ltd., Marylands Avenue, Hemel Hempstead, Hertfordshire, UK
Ecobalances: Holistic View of Automotive Materials, (Abstract) Dow Europe S.A., Bachtobelstrasse 3, CH-8810, Horgen, Switzerland
Engineering Plastics for the Automotive Industry, Hüls (UK) Ltd., Edinburgh House, 43/51 Windsor Road, Slough, Berkshire, SL1 2HL, UK
Engineering Thermoplastic Polymers, BIP Chemicals, PO Box 6, Popes Lane, Oldbury, W. Midlands, B69 4PD, UK
Engineering Thermoplastic Resins, Arco Chemical Co., Philadelphia, PA 19102, USA
Ashbee, K.H.G., *Fundamental Principles of Fiber Reinforced Composites*. Technomic AG, Basel, Switzerland (1989)
Glas-Fiber Reinforcement, Certain Teed Corporation, Valley Forge, PA 19482, USA
Glass Fibre Roving for High-Impact BMC, Owens Corning Fibreglass (GB) Ltd., Crossways, Silwood Road, Sunningdale, Ascot, Berkshire, UK
Glass Mat Reinforced Thermoplastics, Symalit AG, CH-5600, Lensburg, Switzerland (1985)
High Performance Composites, Hitco Materials Division, 1221 E. Dyer Road, Santa Ana. CA 92705, USA (1988)
High Temperature Automotive Resins, Amoco Performance Products, 38c Grove Street, Ridgefield, CT 06877, USA (1990)
High Temperature Resins, Ciba-Geigy, Hawthorne, NY 10532, USA
Hoechst in the Motor Industry, Hoechst UK Ltd., Hoechst House, Salisbury Road, Hounslow, Middlesex TW4 6JH, UK
Daniels, J., *ICI Materials Shape New Metro*, Advance No. 4, ICI Advanced Materials, PO Box 6, Shire Park, Bessemer Road, Welwyn Garden City, Hertfordshire, UK (1990)
La Primavera dell'Auto, Materie Plastiche ed Elastomeri, Editrice MPE, Srl Via del Tritone, 152, 00187, Rome, Italy (1990)

129

130 BIBLIOGRAPHY

Limits of Plastics Uses in Vehicle Construction in the Eighties, VDI-Verlag, GmbH, Dusseldorf (1981)

Low Density and High Resistance Foams, Elastogran GmbH, Postfach 1140, D-2844, Lemforde, Germany (1983)

McConnell, V.P., 'Metal Replacements', *Plastics Design Forum*, Denver, Colorado 80218, USA November/December (1989)

New Thermoplastics Applications & Trends in Motor Vehicle Production, Technical Service Department, Thermoplastics, Bayer AG, Germany

Papers, 15th Congress and Exhibition of Suppliers to the Vehicle Industry, Promexpo Blenehim S.A. SITEV-Forum, 4, Boulevard James-Fazy, PO Box 64, CH-1211, Geneva 11 (1990)

Plastics for Body Panels, (Seminar, June 1-2 1989) The Dow Chemical Co., Bachtobelstrasse 3, CH-8810, Horgan, Switzerland

Plastics for External Car Components, VDI-Verlag GmbH, Dusseldorf (1980)

Plastics in Cars, VDI-Verlag, GmbH, Dusseldorf (1986)

Plastics in Cars, VDI-Verlag, GmbH, Dusseldorf (1983)

Polyamide-imides, Amoco Chemicals Corporation, Illinois 60680, USA

Stute, D., *Production of Large-Area Mouldings for the Motor Industry Using Hot-Runner Moulds*, Technical Service Department, Thermoplastics, Bayer AG, Germany

Reaction – Injection Molding: RIM Systems for Automotive Exterior Parts, Dow Chemical Co., Midland, Michigan 48640, USA

'Reclamation', *British Plastics and Rubber*, pp. 15–18, May (1990)

Boes, D., *Recycling Plastics Fuel Tanks*, BASF AG, D-6700 Ludwigshafen, Germany, June (1990)

Crabtree, D.R., *Recycling in Relation to Thermoplastics*, Extrudaids Ltd., Aston Hill, Lewknor, Oxfordshire, OX9 5SG, UK

Proceedings of Conference on Reinforced Injection Processing – Thermoplastics & Thermosets, Science & Technology Publishers Ltd., Hornchurch, UK (1987)

Wood, R., 'Resin Transfer Molding', *Plastics Machinery & Equipment Magazine*, Denver, Colorado, USA October (1985)

Stainless Steel Fibre Composites, ICI Advanced Materials, PO Box 6, Shire Park, Bessemer Road, Welwyn Garden City, Hertfordshire AL7 1HD, UK

Haart, O.G., 'The Heart of the Bumper', *BASF, K'89 Conference*, Dusseldorf, Germany (1989)

Daniels, J., *Trimming The Nissan Bluebird*, Advance No. 6, ICI Advanced Materials, PO Box 6, Shire Park, Bessemer Road, Welwyn Garden City, Hertfordshire, UK (1989)

Zenoy Composite Polymers, General Electric Plastics BV, Plasticslaan 1, PO Box 117, 4600 AC, Bergen-op-Zoom, Netherlands

APPENDIX: Trade names of some of the more widely used plastics materials in automotive engineering together, where applicable, with their abbreviations and supplier/manufacturers.

Trade name	Material	Abbreviation	Supplier/ Manufacturer
Advanced Composites	Various		Du Pont de
Alcryn	Melt processible rubber		Nemours
Antron	Nylon fibre		International,
Arylon	Polyacrylate resin		S.A.
Bexloy	Thermoplastic eng resin		
Butacite	Polyvinyl butyral	PB	
Dacron	Polyester fibre		
Delrin	Acetal resin		
Elvax	Ethylene vinyl acetate	EVA	
Hypalon	Chorosulphonated polyethylene		
Hytrel	Thermoplastic elastomer		
Kapton	Polyamide film	PI	
Kevlar	Para-aramid fibre		
Minlon	Thermoplastic eng resin		
Nordel	Hydrocarbon rubber		
Rynite	Thermoplastic polyester resin		
Surlyn	Ionomer resin		
Teflon	Fluorocarbon resin		
Vamac	Ethylene acrylic elastomer		
Vespel	Polyimide	PI	
Viton	Fluoro-elastomer		
Zytel	Nylon & GR glass reinforced	PA	
Lupolen	HD- & LD polyethylene	PE	BASF AG
Lacobit	Ethylene copolymer-bitumen	ECB	
Novolen	Polypropylene	PP	
Oppanol	Polyisobutylene	PIB	
GP Polystyrene	Polystyrene	PS	
HI-Polystyrene	Styrene-butadiene-copolymers	SB	
Polystyrene TSG	Styrene-butadiene-copolymers with blowing agent	SB	
Luran	Styrene-acrylonitril-copolymer	SAN	
Luran	Acrylic ester-styrene-acrylonitril-copolymers	ASA	
Terluran	Acrylonitril-butadiene-stryene-copolymers	ABS	
Vinoflex	Polyvinylchloride	PVC	
Vinuran	Polymeric compounds for PVC		

Trade name	Material	Abbreviation	Supplier/ Manufacturer
Ultramid	Polyamide	PA	BASF AG
Ultradur	Polybutylene-terephthalate	PBT	
Ultraform	Polyoxymethylene	POM	
Palatal	Unsaturated polyester resins	UP	
Styropor	Expandable polystyrene	EPS	
Schaumharz	Urea-formaldehyde-resin	UF	
Luvipren	Polyurethane	PUR	
Neopolen	Polyethylene-foam	PE	
Hostalit	Polyvinyl chloride	PVC	Hoechst
Hostalit Z	High impact polyvinyl chloride	PVC–HI	Celanese Plastics Ltd
Hostalen	Polyethylene	PE–HD	
Hostalen PP/Reinforced	Polypropylene	PP	
Hostapren	Chlorinated polyethylene impact modified	PE-C	
Riteflex	Thermoplastic polyester elastomer	TPE	
Hostalen	Ultra high molecular weight polyethylene	PE-UHMW	
Celanex	Polybutylene terephthalate	PBT	
Vandar	Elastomer modified polybutylene terephthalate	PBT-HI	
Impet	Polyethylene terephthalate	PET	
Celanese Nylon	Polyamide 66	PA 66	
Hostaform Kematal	Acetal copolymers	POM	
Celstran	Long fibre reinforced polymers		
Fortron	Polyphenylene sulphide	PPS	
Vectra	Liquid crystalline polymers	LCP	
Hostaflon	Fluoropolymers	PTFE/PFA/FEP/ETFE	
Fluon	Polytetrafluoroethylene (glass/graphite reinforced)	PTFE	ICI Advanced Materials (High temperature engine compartment use)
Lubricomp	Lubricated thermoplastics	PTFE	
Maranyl	Polyamide 6 & 66 (various grades)	PA	
Procom	Polypropylene (various grades)	PP	
Propathene	Copolymers/ homopolymers	PP	

Trade name	Material	Abbreviation	Supplier/ Manufacturer
Verton	Long fibre reinforcement (including polyamide 66)		ICI Advanced Materials (contd.)
Victrex	Polyethersulphone & Polyetheretherketone (reinforced/lubricated grades)		
Trogamid	Polyamide grade	PA6-3-T	Hüls (UK) Ltd
Vestamid	Polyamide (fuel resist, etc.)	PA12	
Vestodur	Polybutylene-terephthalate (high heat deflection)	PBT	
Vestoran		MPPE	
Pulse A20-95 (medium impact)	Polycarbonate/ acryonitrile-butadiene-styrene	PC-ABS	Dow Chemical Co
Pulse A30-105 (high impact)	Polycarbonate/ acryonitrile-butadiene-styrene	PC-ABS	
Magnum resins	Acrylonitrile-butadiene-styrene	ABS	
Calibre resins	Polycarbonate	PC	
Tyril resins	Styrene-acrylonitrile	SAN	
Styron resins	Polystyrene	PS	
Derakane (for SMC)	Vinyl ester		
Advanced composites	Various		
Beetle Nylon 6 & 66	Polyamide	PA	BIP Chemicals Ltd
Beetle PET	Polyethylene terephthalate	PET	
Beetle PBT	Polybutylene-terephthalate	PBT	
Beetle Polycarbonate	Polycarbonate	PC	
Lexan	Polycarbonate	PC	GE Plastics, UK
Noryl	Modified PPO	PPO/PS	
Valox	Thermoplastic polyester	PBTP & PET	
Cycolac	Acrylonitrile butadiene styrene	ABS	
Cycoloy	Polycarbonate/ABS blend	PC/ABS	
Xenoy	Polycarbonate/polyester blends	PC/PBT etc	
Noryl GTX		PA/PPO	
Ultem	Polyetherimide	PEI	
Supec	Polyphenylene sulphide	PPS	
Lomod	Polyester		
Technopolymer structures	Thermoplastic composites		

Trade name	Material	Abbreviation	Supplier/Manufacturer
Baypren	Orlorprene rubber	OR	Bayer AG
Perbunan N	Nitrile-butadine rubber	NBR	
Therban	Hydrogenated nitrile butadiene	HNBR	
Levapren	Ethylene vinyl acetate rubber	EVM	
Buna CB	Butadiene rubber	BR	(Rubbers)
Baystal	Styrene-butadiene latex	SBR	
Pyratex	Vinyl pyridine latex	PSBR	
Baycoll	Polyester or polyester polyols		
Desmocoll	Hydroxyl polyurethanes		
Desmodur	Polyisocynates		
Baydur			
Bayflex			
Bayfill			(Polyure-
Bayfit			thanes)
Baynat			
Baytherm			
Apec		PAR	
Apec HT		PC	
Bayblend		PC + ABS; PC + ASA	
Durethan		PA	
Makrolon		PC	
Novodur		ABS, ASA	(Plastics)
Pocan		PBT, PBT mod	
Tedur		PPS	
Optipol		PC basis	
Desmopan		TPU	
Gusspolyamid		PA 6 G	
Makrofol			
Shell polypropylene		PP	Shell International Chemical Co Ltd
Shell Low density polyethylene		LDPE	
Shell polystyrene		PS	
Styrocell expandable polystyrene		PS	
Cariflex TR	Thermoplastic rubber		
Cariflex SBR, BR & IR			
Caradol polyols			

Index

Air filter, Porsche 959   33
Automatic gear shift   44
Blow moulding   19
  body panels   20, 107
  fuel tanks   97
  inserts   20
  radiator cooling reservoir   41
  radiator expansion tanks   39
Body panels, blow moulded   20
Bodywork   62–92
  "all purpose" vehicle   63–67
  composite construction   68
  flexible coatings   68
  in-line painting   62
Brake pads   43, 50
Braking systems   50, 51, 54
Bulk moulding compound
  (BMC)   116
Bumpers   54, 61, 71, 72
  air dams   55
  body colour bumpers   55, 60, 61
  "just in time" production   58
  low impact damage   55
  moulding   56
  trim   59
Camshaft advance/retard system   33
Camshaft covers   31
Carbon fibre   117
  tape, woven fabrics   128
Carburettor bodies   35
Carpets   90–92
Chassis   47
Clutch facings   43
Co-extrusion   30
Composite engines   33
Compression moulding   8
Cooling system   39
Door development   73
Doors   70
Dumping (see recycling)   93
Electrics/electronics   27
Engine snow shield   45, 46
Engineering polymers   3, 52, 53
Environmental considerations
  (see recycling)   93
Extrusion   18, 19
  corrugated pipe   19
  crosshead system, sheathing   19, 27

two-component production   19
Fabric finishes (see seating)   25
Fascias   77–80
Fluor-elastomer seals   35
Formula 1 gear box selector   44
Fuel systems   4, 19, 27, 35
Fuel tanks   35–39
  anti gas/liquid permeation systems   36
  drop tests   36
  leaded/unleaded fuel acceptance
    unit   39
  post moulding fluorination
    system   20, 36
  production US   36
  reclamation   97
Gaskets
  engine life   31
  para amide coated   31
  semi-flexible   31
Gear shift mechanism   43
Glass fibre mat   113–116
Glass fibre reinforced
  thermoplastics   115–117
Glass fibre roving   113
Header tanks   39
Headliners   91
Injection moulding   5–18
  composite components,
    sealing   17, 18
  fountain flow effect   14
  fusible core system   18, 35
  gas melt system   13
  multi-coloured materials   14, 15
  multi-materials   10
  polymer compatibility   12
  "quick change" mould system   4
  reinforced polyesters (ZMC
    process)   16, 23, 24, 70
  structural foam   8
  thermosets   7
Integrated bumpers   72
"Just in time" production (JIT)   4, 58
Leaf spring development   47, 49
Lights   82–86
  glass replacement   82
  sandwich moulding/metallizing
       83, 84
  scratch resistance treatment   83

Liquid/gas permeation   19
Multi-layer extrusion system   36
Para amide coated piston rings   31
Plating on plastics   24
Plug leads   30
Powertrain   27
Production methods (*see*
    Injection moulding
Racing car research   44, 109–111
Radiator expansion tanks   39
Rear light clusters   84
Recycling   93–101
    batteries   98
    blow moulded fuel tanks   97
    composites   98, 99
    dumping   93
    environmental considerations   93
    material selection   93
    polymer identification   94
    shredding   93, 101
Reinforcement   112–127
Road wheels   51, 52
Rocker panels   70
Rotational moulding   21, 22
Safety   73–77
    "active" and "passive"   73, 74
    damage limitation   74
Screens   80–82

Seating   86–92
    design flexibility, fabric finish   86
    foam-in-fabric systems   86, 87
    weight savings   86
Sheet extrusion   19
Sheet moulding compound   114
Side lights   84, 85
Soft ends   75–77
    deformation/recovery   76, 77
    front and rear concept   76, 77
    physical requirements   75
Special construction prototypes
                                                  102–111
Spoilers   71, 73
Springs   47, 49
Steering   50
Steering wheels, glass reinforced   50
Suspensions   47
Tailgates   70
Transmission   43–45
Vacuum and pressure forming   21
Welding   22, 85
Wheel trim   52, 53
    paintability   53
    special finishes   54
Windows   80, 81
Windscreen sealing   80
Wiper blade   81, 82